Common Core Writing to Te...

MW00624016

Table of Contents

Introduction

What Is the Common Core?

The Common Core State Standards are an initiative by states to set shared, consistent, and clear criteria for what students are expected to learn. This helps teachers and parents know what they need to do to help students. The standards are designed to be rigorous and pertinent to the real world. They reflect the knowledge and skills that young people need for success in college and careers.

If your state has joined the Common Core State Standards Initiative, then teachers are required to incorporate these standards into their lesson plans. Students need targeted practice in order to meet grade-level standards and expectations, and thereby be promoted to the next grade.

What Does It Mean to Write to Texts?

One of the most important instructional shifts in the Common Core State Standards is writing to texts, or sources. What exactly does this mean? Haven't standardized assessments always used reading texts as a springboard to writing? Yes, but the required writing hasn't always been DEPENDENT on the key ideas and details in a text.

A prompt that is non-text-dependent asks students to rely on prior knowledge or experience. In fact, students could likely carry out the writing without reading the text at all. The writing does not need to include ideas, information, and key vocabulary from the text.

Writing to texts requires students to analyze, clarify, and cite information they read in the text. The writing reveals whether students have performed a close reading, because it is designed to elicit ideas, information, and key vocabulary from the text as well as students' own evidence-based inferences and conclusions. These are all skills that prepare them for the grades ahead, college, the workplace, and real-world applications in their adult daily lives.

An example of a passage with non-text-dependent and text-dependent sample prompts is provided on page 3.

Common Core Writing to Texts Grade 6 • ©2014 Newmark Learning, LLC

Sample Passage

Simple and Compound Machines

1. A simple machine is a tool that does work with one movement. Like all machines, a simple machine makes work easier. It has few or no moving parts and uses energy to do work. A lever, a wedge, a screw, a pulley, a wheel and axle, and an inclined plane are all simple machines.

2. You use simple machines all the time, too. If you have ever played on a seesaw or walked up a ramp, then you have used a simple machine. If you have opened a door, eaten with a spoon, cut with scissors, or zipped up a zipper, you have used a simple machine.

3. A compound machine is made of two or more simple machines. For example, the pedals, wheels, and gears on a bicycle are wheels and axles, and the hand brakes on the handlebars are levers. Cars, airplanes, watches, and washing machines are also examples of compound machines. Compound machines are very useful because they can do the work of many simple machines at the same time.

4. Life would be very different if we did not have machines. Work would be much harder, and playing wouldn't be as much fun.

Standard	Sample Prompt: Non-Text-Dependent	Sample Prompt: Text-Dependent
W.6.1 (Argument)	Do you prefer zippers, buttons, buckles, or another type of fastener for your clothing? Why?	The author makes three claims in the last paragraph. Choose one of the claims, tell whether you agree or disagree, and support your opinion with evidence from the text.
W.6.2 (Informative/ Explanatory)	Think about a machine you have used to do a task. How did you use it? How did using the machine make the task easier?	Compare and contrast simple and compound machines. Use details from the text to support your explanation.
W.6.3 (Narrative)	Write a story in which a character invents a machine that no one has seen or heard of before.	Imagine that all the machines mentioned in the passage disappeared for twenty-four hours. Write a journal entry about how your life was different that day and what you learned.

Using This Book

How Does This Book Help Students?

This book is organized into four main sections: Writing Mini-Lessons, Practice Texts with Prompts, Graphic Organizers and Checklists, and Rubrics and Assessments. All mini-lessons and practice pages are self-contained and may be used in any order that meets the needs of students. The elements of this book work together to provide students with the tools they need to be able to master the range of skills and application as required by the Common Core.

1. Mini-Lessons for Argument, Informative/Explanatory, and Narrative Writing

Writing mini-lessons prepare students to use writing as a way to state and support opinions, demonstrate understanding of the subjects they are studying, and convey real and imagined experiences. The mini-lessons are organized in the order of the standards, but you may wish to do them with your class in an order that matches your curriculum. For each type of writing the first mini-lesson covers responding to one text, while the second mini-lesson models how to respond to multiple texts.

Each mini-lesson begins with a lesson plan that provides step-by-step instruction.

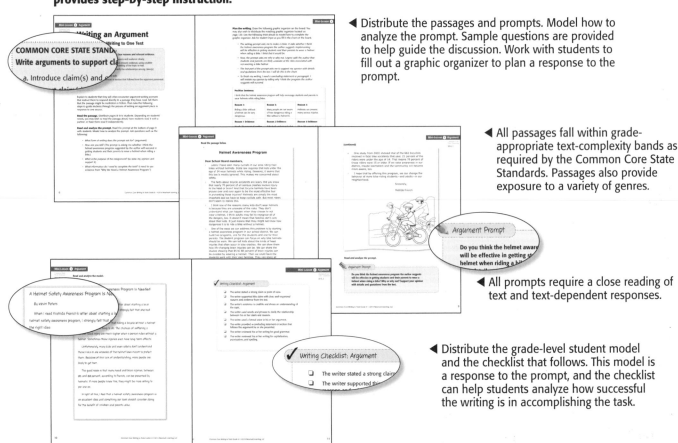

◀ Distribute the passages and prompts. Model how to analyze the prompt. Sample questions are provided to help guide the discussion. Work with students to fill out a graphic organizer to plan a response to the prompt.

◀ All passages fall within grade-appropriate text-complexity bands as required by the Common Core State Standards. Passages also provide exposure to a variety of genres.

◀ All prompts require a close reading of text and text-dependent responses.

◀ Distribute the grade-level student model and the checklist that follows. This model is a response to the prompt, and the checklist can help students analyze how successful the writing is in accomplishing the task.

2. Practice Texts with Prompts

Passages and prompts provide students with real experience writing to a single text and multiple texts. The first ten lessons require students to respond to one text. The last ten require students to respond to multiple texts.

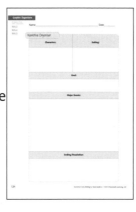
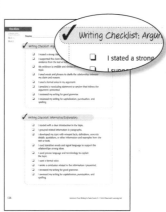

Each passage or pair of passages is followed by three text-dependent prompts: Argument, Informative/Explanatory, and Narrative. You may wish to assign a particular prompt, have students choose one, or have them execute each type of writing over a longer period of time.

For more information on how to use this section, see page 48.

3. Graphic Organizers and Checklists

For each type of writing, you can distribute a corresponding graphic organizer and checklist to help students plan and evaluate their writing.

4. Rubrics and Assessments

The section includes Evaluation Rubrics to guide your assessment and scoring of students' responses. Based on your observations of students' writing, use the differentiated rubrics. These are designed to help you conduct meaningful conferences with students and will help differentiate your interactions to match students' needs.

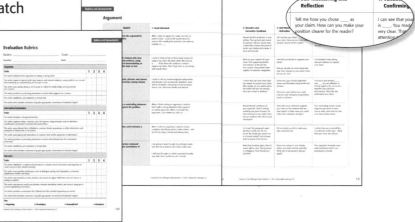

For each score a student receives in the Evaluation Rubrics, responsive prompts are provided. These gradual-release prompts scaffold writers toward mastery of each writing type.

Writing an Argument

Mini-Lesson 1: Writing to One Text

COMMON CORE STATE STANDARD W.6.1
Write arguments to support claims with clear reasons and relevant evidence.

a. Introduce claim(s) and organize the reasons and evidence clearly.

b. Support claim(s) with clear reasons and relevant evidence, using credible sources and demonstrating an understanding of the topic or text.

c. Use words, phrases, and clauses to clarify the relationships among claim(s) and reasons.

d. Establish and maintain a formal style.

e. Provide a concluding statement or section that follows from the argument presented.

Explain to students that they will often encounter argument-writing prompts that instruct them to respond directly to a passage they have read. Tell them that the passage might be nonfiction or fiction. Then take the following steps to guide students through the process of writing an argument piece in response to one source.

Read the passage. Distribute pages 8–9 to students. Depending on students' needs, you may wish to read the passage aloud, have students read it with a partner, or have them read it independently.

Read and analyze the prompt. Read the prompt at the bottom of page 9 with students. Model how to analyze the prompt. Ask questions such as the following:

- *What form of writing does the prompt ask for?* (argument)

- *How can you tell?* (The prompt is asking me whether I think the helmet awareness progress suggested by the author will succeed in getting students and their parents to wear a helmet when riding a bike.)

- *What is the purpose of the assignment?* (to state my opinion and support it)

- *What information do I need to complete the task?* (I need to use evidence from "Helmet Awareness Program.")

Plan the writing. Draw the following graphic organizer on the board. You may also wish to distribute the matching graphic organizer located on page 120. Use the following think-alouds to model how to complete the graphic organizer. Ask for student input as you fill in the chart on the board.

- *The writing prompt asks me to make a claim. It asks whether I think the helmet awareness program the author suggests implementing will be effective in getting students and their parents to wear a helmet when riding a bike. I think that it would be.*

- *Next, the prompt asks me why or why not. I agree with the author that students and parents are likely unaware of the risks associated with not wearing a bike helmet.*

- *The last part of the prompt asks me to support my opinion with details and quotations from the text. I will do this in the chart.*

- *To finish my writing, I need a concluding statement or paragraph. I will restate my opinion by telling why I think the program the author suggests will succeed.*

Position Sentence:

I think that the helmet awareness program will help encourage students and parents to wear helmets while riding bikes.

Reason 1:	**Reason 2:**	**Reason 3:**
Riding a bike without a helmet can be very dangerous.	Many people are not aware of how dangerous riding a bike without a helmet is.	Helmets can prevent many serious injuries.
Reason 1 Evidence:	**Reason 2 Evidence:**	**Reason 3 Evidence:**
Nearly 70 percent of crashes involved head/brain injuries. Brain injuries can be life-changing.	Kids don't understand what can happen when they choose not wear a helmet. Most helmet laws focus only on young people.	85 to 88 percent of brain injuries can be prevented with a helmet.

Restate position:

I believe that a helmet awareness program should be started to encourage students and their parents to wear helmets while riding bikes.

Read and analyze the model. Distribute the student writing model and checklist on pages 10–11 to students. Read them aloud. Discuss with students whether or not the writer was successful at accomplishing the task. Ask students to complete the checklist as you discuss the argument.

Read the passage below.

Helmet Awareness Program

Dear School Board Members,

1. Lately I have seen many cyclists in our area riding their bikes without helmets. State law requires that kids under the age of 14 wear helmets while riding. However, it seems that this law is mostly ignored. This makes me concerned about safety.

2. The facts about bicycle accidents are scary. Did you know that nearly 70 percent of all serious crashes involve injury to the head or brain? And that bicycle helmets have been proven over and over again to be the most effective tool in preventing these injuries? Helmets are simply the most important tool we have to keep cyclists safe. But most riders don't seem to realize this.

3. I think one of the reasons many kids don't wear helmets is because they are unaware of the risks. They don't understand what can happen when they choose to not wear a helmet. I think adults may fail to recognize all of the dangers, too. It doesn't mean that families don't care about their kids. It just means that they might not know how dangerous it is to ride a bike without a helmet.

4. One of the ways we can address this problem is by starting a helmet awareness program in our school district. We can build two programs, one for the students and one for their parents. The student program can focus on why bike helmets should be worn. We can tell kids about the kinds of head injuries that often occur in bike crashes. We can show them how life-changing brain injuries can be. We can share the studies showing that 85 to 88 percent of brain injuries can be avoided by wearing a helmet. Then we could have the students work with their own families. They can share all the information they received. They can also sign a contract agreeing to wear a helmet whenever they ride a bike.

5. I'd also like to see our program go one step further. Even though most states have passed helmet laws, these laws are directed mostly at riders under the age of 14. While it's very important to protect this group, older riders need protection, too.

(continued)

(continued)

6. One study from 2002 showed that of the 662 bicyclists involved in fatal bike accidents that year, 21 percent of the riders were under the age of 14. That means 79 percent of those riders were 15 or older. If we raise awareness in our district, maybe lawmakers and the community will become more aware, too.

7. I hope that by offering this program, we can change the behavior of more bike-riding students—and adults—in our neighborhood.

Sincerely,

Matilda French

Read and analyze the prompt.

Argument Prompt

Do you think the helmet awareness program the author suggests will be effective in getting students and their parents to wear a helmet when riding a bike? Why or why not? Support your opinion with details and quotations from the text.

Read and analyze the model.

A Helmet Safety Awareness Program Is Needed

By Kevin Peters

When I read Matilda French's letter about starting a local helmet safety awareness program, I strongly felt that she had the right idea.

She correctly pointed out that riding a bicycle without a helmet is a very dangerous thing to do. The chances of suffering a serious head injury are much higher when a person rides without a helmet. Sometimes those injuries even have long-term effects.

Unfortunately, many kids and even adults don't understand these risks or are unaware of the helmet laws meant to protect them. Because of this lack of understanding, more people are likely to get hurt.

The good news is that many head and brain injuries, between 85 and 88 percent, according to French, can be prevented by helmets. If more people knew this, they might be more willing to put one on.

In light of this, I feel that a helmet safety awareness program is an excellent idea and something our town should consider doing for the benefit of children and parents alike.

COMMON CORE
STATE STANDARD
W.6.1

✔ Writing Checklist: Argument

❏   The writer stated a strong claim or point of view.

❏   The writer supported this claim with clear, well-organized reasons and evidence from the text.

❏   The writer's evidence is credible and shows an understanding of the topic.

❏   The writer used words and phrases to clarify the relationship between his or her claim and reasons.

❏   The writer used a formal voice in his or her argument.

❏   The writer provided a concluding statement or section that follows the argument he or she presented.

❏   The writer reviewed his or her writing for good grammar.

❏   The writer reviewed his or her writing for capitalization, punctuation, and spelling.

COMMON CORE
STATE STANDARD
W.6.1

Writing an Argument

Mini-Lesson 2: **Writing to Multiple Texts**

> **COMMON CORE STATE STANDARD W.6.1**
> **Write arguments to support claims with clear reasons and relevant evidence.**
> a. Introduce claim(s) and organize the reasons and evidence clearly.
> b. Support claim(s) with clear reasons and relevant evidence, using credible sources and demonstrating an understanding of the topic or text.
> c. Use words, phrases, and clauses to clarify the relationships among claim(s) and reasons.
> d. Establish and maintain a formal style.
> e. Provide a concluding statement or section that follows from the argument presented.

Explain to students that they will often encounter writing prompts that instruct them to respond directly to more than one passage. For example, they might have to read two informational passages about the same topic or two fiction passages by the same author. Then take the following steps to guide students through the process of writing an argument in response to multiple texts.

Read the passages. Distribute pages 14–17 to students. Depending on students' needs, you may wish to read the passages aloud, have students read them with a partner, or have them read the passages independently.

Read and analyze the prompt. Read the prompt at the bottom of page 17 with students. Model how to analyze the prompt. Ask questions such as the following:

- *What form of writing does the prompt ask for?* (argument)

- *How can you tell?* (The prompt is asking which speech I agree with more and why.)

- *What is the purpose of the assignment?* (to state my opinion and support it with evidence)

- *What information do I need to complete the task?* (I need to use evidence from both "Vote 'No' for Vending Machines" and "Show Support for Snack Machines.")

Plan the writing. Draw the following graphic organizer on the board. You may also wish to distribute the matching graphic organizer located on page 121. Use the following think-alouds to model how to complete the graphic organizer. Ask for student input as you fill in the chart on the board.

- *The writing prompt asks me to form an opinion about which speech I agree with more. I agree more with "Vote 'No' for Vending Machines" because I think having vending machines in school will only encourage students to learn poor eating habits.*

- *Now I will think about the second part of the prompt. It asks me to support my opinion with reasons from the speeches and my own ideas.*

- *I will record my reasons and my evidence in the chart.*

- *To finish my writing, I need a concluding statement or paragraph. I will restate my opinion by explaining why I agree more with the presenter of the first speech.*

Position Sentence:		
I agree with the ideas expressed in "Vote 'No' for Vending Machines."		
Reason 1: Diet is important to a healthy lifestyle.	**Reason 2:** Vending machines would defeat the purpose of government food guidelines.	**Reason 3:** Vending-machine foods would negatively affect classroom behavior.
Reason 1 Evidence: Children are developing health issues because of their eating habits. Poor diet choices are dangerous for people now and in the future. Poor diet choices can lead to heart disease.	**Reason 2 Evidence:** Vending machines stock unhealthy foods. The government has worked to establish healthy food service guidelines for schools.	**Reason 3 Evidence:** Caffeine and sugar make kids hyper and inattentive in class. Vending machines would give them easy access to foods with high levels of caffeine and sugar.
Restate position:		
I believe that installing vending machines in school would be a bad, unhealthy choice for students.		

Read and analyze the model. Distribute the student writing model and checklist on pages 18–19 to students. Read them aloud. Discuss with students whether or not the writer was successful at accomplishing the task. Ask them to complete the checklist as you discuss the argument.

COMMON CORE
STATE STANDARD
W.6.1

Read the passages.

Vote "No" for Vending Machines

1.   Welcome, fellow parents and teachers. Thank you for joining us at this special meeting of the Parent Teacher Association.

2.   As many of you know, some members of the PTA have proposed installing vending machines in our schools. The proceeds from the vending machines would help pay for after-school clubs, field trips, and other programs. I appreciate those who developed this plan for your eager participation in the PTA. I usually applaud any efforts that work toward giving our children a more well-rounded education. However, installing vending machines in our schools is not the way to achieve this goal.

3.   Over the past few years, doctors and scientists have stressed the importance of diet and exercise in leading a healthy lifestyle. More and more of our children are developing serious health problems earlier in life. Studies show that unhealthy eating habits carry over from childhood to adulthood. These habits lead to serious conditions, such as heart disease. Easy access to vending machines will only contribute to the health problems our children face. Vending machines will tempt students during the only hours each day when parents are not available to guide them toward healthier choices.

4.   In the fight against unhealthy habits, government leaders have created new guidelines to help us teach our children to make healthy choices. They have worked to make school breakfasts and lunches healthier. Meals served in our cafeterias today have fewer calories. Foods contain less sugar, salt, and fat. We can finally rest assured that the meals our children receive at school are wholesome

(continued)

Common Core Writing to Texts Grade 6 • ©2014 Newmark Learning, LLC

(continued)

and healthy. Installing vending machines filled with chips, candy bars, and sugary drinks will ruin this progress.

5.   In addition, many students have trouble paying attention during class. The last thing these kids need is more caffeine and sugar. Giving them access to vending machines filled with sugary drinks and snacks loaded with fat could make these problems worse.

6.   Parents and teachers, I'm in favor of trying to give our children the best, most well-rounded education possible. I realize that installing vending machines in our schools will provide us with money we could use toward important educational opportunities. However, these vending machines will result in more harm than good. Ask yourself: Are my children's lives really worth a few bucks earned from vending machines?

(continue to next passage)

(continued)

Show Support for Snack Machines

1.   Good evening, everyone. Thanks again for joining us tonight to discuss an important topic: installing vending machines in our schools.

2.   Imagine sending your son or daughter on a field trip to Washington, D.C. to see Congress in action. Imagine providing your child with the newest, fastest computers available. Imagine giving your children's teachers the supplies they need to truly make learning come alive in the classroom. All this is possible—for a price. We have the opportunity to raise tens of thousands of dollars to help pay for special trips and the latest technologies to improve our children's learning. It all starts with installing vending machines in our schools.

3.   I know some of you are opposed to this idea. You say that soda and snack machines will ruin our children's health. You say that these machines will tempt our children to choose "bad" foods over "good" ones. Who are we to say which foods are "bad" and "good"? It's acceptable to eat almost all foods in moderation. Who are we to say which foods students and teachers can and cannot eat? It should be up to each individual to choose the foods he or she wants.

4.   The important word there is "choose." Vending machines do not have to contain only soda and cookies. Many vending machine companies tailor the machines to include exactly what their clients want. Therefore, we can request a variety of snacks. Students and teachers can choose which ones they want to eat. Snack machines may contain some standbys like chips and chocolate, but they can also contain apples, granola bars, and low-fat yogurt. Soft drink machines may include regular, diet, and caffeine-free options, as well as water and fruit juice. If you have talked to your son or daughter about health and nutrition, then he or she should know when to choose an apple over a chocolate bar or skim milk over soda.

5.   As a parent, I have learned that children are like bloodhounds when it comes to snack foods. They will look for cupcakes and nacho chips hidden in the darkest corner

(continued)

(continued)

of the highest cabinet. It's not uncommon for students to leave campus to buy snacks elsewhere. When students leave school to buy snacks and drinks, they put their safety at risk. Likewise, when students stop to purchase these foods on their way to school, they increase their chance of arriving late. By installing vending machines on campus, we will decrease the temptation to seek snacks elsewhere. Having these foods available at school will make our children safer in the long run.

6. In closing, I'd just like to remind you of all the good you can do for your kids with the money raised from vending machines. Give your children the best education they can get—the education they deserve. Please vote to install vending machines in our schools.

Read and analyze the prompt.

Argument Prompt

Imagine that you were a parent in the audience when these speeches were delivered. Based on the details and evidence in these two speeches, which speech do you agree with more and why? Support your claim with reasons from both speeches.

Read and analyze the model.

"No" to Vending Machines

By Carol Miller

At the most recent PTA meeting, we heard arguments for and against installing vending machines in our schools. Both of the speeches we heard had their merits, but I have to agree with the position that vending machines are probably not a good idea.

First, as we heard, a proper diet is an important part of a healthy lifestyle and a critical lesson for our children to learn. Poor diet and unhealthy eating habits are dangerous for our children now and in the future. Heart disease could be the result. We must be sure to avoid allowing them to make risky choices through patronizing vending machines.

Further, because vending machines usually stock unhealthy food items, such as candy and potato chips, their use would interfere with the healthy eating guidelines established by the government. The government has worked hard to pass these guidelines to protect our children, and we should respect them.

Finally, the immediate effects of vending machine foods will likely be bad for the classroom learning experience. Vending machines offer easy access to foods loaded with sugar and caffeine. These substances make it harder for students to concentrate and lead to more classroom interruptions.

For these reasons, I feel we should not allow vending machines to be installed in our schools.

✔ Writing Checklist: Argument

❑ The writer stated a strong claim or point of view.

❑ The writer supported this claim with clear, well-organized reasons and evidence from the text.

❑ The writer's evidence is credible and shows an understanding of the topic.

❑ The writer used words and phrases to clarify the relationship between his or her claim and reasons.

❑ The writer used a formal voice in his or her argument.

❑ The writer provided a concluding statement or section that follows the argument he or she presented.

❑ The writer reviewed his or her writing for good grammar.

❑ The writer reviewed his or her writing for capitalization, punctuation, and spelling.

COMMON CORE
STATE STANDARD
W.6.2

Writing an Informative/ Explanatory Text

Mini-Lesson 3: **Writing to One Text**

COMMON CORE STATE STANDARD W.6.2

Write informative/explanatory texts to examine a topic and convey ideas, concepts, and information through the selection, organization, and analysis of relevant content.

a. Introduce a topic; organize ideas, concepts, and information, using strategies such as definition, classification, comparison/contrast, and cause/effect; include formatting (e.g., headings), graphics (e.g., charts, tables), and multimedia when useful to aiding comprehension.

b. Develop the topic with relevant facts, definitions, concrete details, quotations, or other information and examples.

c. Use appropriate transitions to clarify the relationships among ideas and concepts.

d. Use precise language and domain-specific vocabulary to inform about or explain the topic.

e. Establish and maintain a formal style.

f. Provide a concluding statement or section that follows from the information or explanation presented.

Explain to students that they will often encounter informative/explanatory writing prompts that instruct them to respond directly to a passage they have read. Tell them that the passage might be an informational passage or fiction. Then take the following steps to guide students through the process of informative/explanatory writing in response to one text.

Read the passage. Distribute pages 22–23 to students. Depending on students' needs, you may wish to read the passage aloud, have students read it with a partner, or have them read it independently.

Read and analyze the prompt. Read the prompt at the bottom of page 23 with students. Model how to analyze the prompt. Ask questions such as the following:

- *What form of writing does the prompt ask for?* (informative/ explanatory)

- *How can you tell?* (The prompt is asking me to summarize why the Seikan Tunnel was important but difficult to build.)

- *What is the purpose of the assignment?* (to explain a topic through a summary)

- *What information do I need to complete the task?* (I need to use evidence from the passage "Seikan Tunnel.")

COMMON CORE
STATE STANDARD
W.6.2

Plan the writing. Draw the following graphic organizer on the board. You may also wish to distribute the matching graphic organizer located on page 122. Use the following think-alouds to model how to complete the graphic organizer. Ask for student input as you fill in the chart on the board.

- *The writing prompt asks me to summarize why the Seikan Tunnel was important, yet difficult to build. The prompt asks me to do this using specific details from the passage.*

- *I will record my evidence in the chart.*

- *To finish my writing, I need a concluding statement or paragraph.*

Main Idea: The author says the Seikan Tunnel made travel easier.
Evidence/details: The tunnel linked Honshu and Hokkaido. **Evidence/details:** Travelers had to take a ferry before the tunnel was built.
Main Idea: The author says that building the Seikan Tunnel was difficult.
Evidence/details: It took thousands of people to build the tunnel. **Evidence/details:** It also took 150,000 tons of steel and around 3,000 explosives. **Evidence/details:** It cost $7 billion to build the tunnel. **Evidence/details:** Workers had to be careful not to set off an earthquake. **Evidence/details:** Accidents claimed thirty-four lives during its construction.

Read and analyze the model. Distribute the student writing model and checklist on pages 24–25 to students. Read them aloud. Discuss with students whether or not the writer was successful at accomplishing this task. Ask them to complete the checklist as you discuss the informative/explanatory text.

COMMON CORE
STATE STANDARD

W.6.2

Read the passage below.

The Seikan Tunnel

1.   The Seikan Tunnel is located underwater in the Tsugaru Strait of Japan. This important waterway connects the Sea of Japan to the Pacific Ocean. It is situated between Honshu, Japan's main island, and Hokkaido Island to the north. The Seikan Tunnel is the longest rail tunnel in the world, and the deepest. The tunnel is about 33.5 miles in total length. Nearly 14 of those miles are located 800 feet below sea level.

2.   The Seikan Tunnel project was sponsored by Japanese National Railways, a government entity. Building the Seikan Tunnel was an enormous project that took more than twenty years. Because the Tsugaru Strait is considered a major earthquake zone, construction was slow. Nearly 3,000 workers were employed at a time. Crews had to be very careful about blasting near the seafloor while building the tunnel for fear of setting off an earthquake. The crews eventually used more than 150,000 tons of steel and nearly 3,000 explosives. Work on the tunnel was finally completed in 1988. The tunnel was opened to the public in March of that year.

3.   The tunnel project was costly. The Japanese government spent more than $7 billion over the life of the project. The project had other costs as well. Thirty-four railroad workers lost their lives during construction.

(continued)

Common Core Writing to Texts Grade 6 • ©2014 Newmark Learning, LLC

(continued)

The project experienced many floods, cave-ins, and other accidents.

4.   The tunnel was originally built to provide travelers with an easier way to get back and forth between Honshu and Hokkaido. Before the tunnel was built, travelers had to take a ferry to get from one island to the other. The ferry took nearly four hours. In contrast, the tunnel runs the Shinkansen, Japan's high-speed bullet train. The rail trip between the two islands now takes about 50 minutes.

5.   Before the tunnel construction was completed, however, people started traveling between the islands by air. This mode of travel takes about as long as the railway and costs about the same. Therefore, the rail line is not used as much as originally thought. Still, the tunnel is considered a technological marvel and one of the greatest examples of modern engineering in the world.

About the Seikan Tunnel

Where It's Located:

Tsugaru Strait, Japan

When Completed:

March 1988

Length:

33.5 miles

Depth:

800 feet below sea level

Read and analyze the prompt.

Informative/Explanatory Prompt

Using specific details from the passage, "The Seikan Tunnel," summarize why the Seikan Tunnel was important, yet difficult, to build.

COMMON CORE
STATE STANDARD

W.6.2

Read and analyze the model.

The Important Cost of the Seikan Tunnel

By Sonia Escobar

The author of "The Seikan Tunnel" makes it clear that the tunnel was an important but very difficult project.

The tunnel is important mainly because of how it helps travelers. It connects the main Japanese island, called Honshu, with the island of Hokkaido. Before the tunnel, the only way to reach the island was by a long ferry trip. The tunnel made the trip much shorter.

The construction of the tunnel, however, was very difficult. Thousands of workers had to use 150,000 tons of steel and about 3,000 explosives to get it built. The workers also had to be very careful to not set off an earthquake because the tunnel was near an earthquake zone. A series of accidents during construction of the tunnel claimed thirty-four lives. In all, the tunnel cost about $7 billion.

COMMON CORE
STATE STANDARD
W.6.2

✔ ## Writing Checklist: Informative/Explanatory

❏ The writer started with a clear introduction to the topic.

❏ The writer grouped related information in paragraphs.

❏ The writer developed the topic with relevant facts, definitions, concrete details, quotations, or other information and examples from the text.

❏ The writer used transition words and signal language to support the relationships among ideas.

❏ The writer used precise language and terminology to explain the topic.

❏ The writer used a formal voice.

❏ The writer wrote a conclusion related to the information he or she presented.

❏ The writer reviewed his or her writing for good grammar.

❏ The writer reviewed his or her writing for capitalization, punctuation, and spelling.

COMMON CORE
STATE STANDARD
W.6.2

Writing an Informative/ Explanatory Text

Mini-Lesson 4: Writing to Multiple Texts

COMMON CORE STATE STANDARD W.6.2

Write informative/explanatory texts to examine a topic and convey ideas, concepts, and information through the selection, organization, and analysis of relevant content.

a. Introduce a topic; organize ideas, concepts, and information, using strategies such as definition, classification, comparison/contrast, and cause/effect; include formatting (e.g., headings), graphics (e.g., charts, tables), and multimedia when useful to aiding comprehension.

b. Develop the topic with relevant facts, definitions, concrete details, quotations, or other information and examples.

c. Use appropriate transitions to clarify the relationships among ideas and concepts.

d. Use precise language and domain-specific vocabulary to inform about or explain the topic.

e. Establish and maintain a formal style.

f. Provide a concluding statement or section that follows from the information or explanation presented.

Explain to students that they will often encounter writing prompts that instruct them to respond directly to more than one passage. For example, they might have to read two informational passages about the same topic or two fiction passages by the same author. Then take the following steps to guide students through the process of writing an informative/explanatory piece in response to multiple texts.

Read the passages. Distribute pages 28–31 to students. Depending on students' needs, you may wish to read the passages aloud, have students read them with a partner, or have them read the passages independently.

Read and analyze the prompt. Read the prompt at the bottom of page 31 with students. Model how to analyze the prompt. Ask questions such as the following:

- *What form of writing does the prompt ask for?* (informative/explanatory)

- *How can you tell?* (The prompt is asking me to explain something and provide information.)

- *What is the purpose of the assignment?* (to explain a topic and give information about it)

- *What information do I need to complete the task?* (I need to use evidence from the passage "Three Branches of Government" and the passage "Checks and Balances.")

Common Core Writing to Texts Grade 6 • ©2014 Newmark Learning, LLC

COMMON CORE
STATE STANDARD
W.6.2

Plan the writing. Draw the following graphic organizer on the board. You may also wish to distribute the matching graphic organizer located on page 123. Use the following think-alouds to model how to complete the graphic organizer. Ask for student input as you fill in the chart on the board.

- *The writing prompt asks me to use information from both passages to explain the function of the executive and legislative branches of the U.S. government and the checks and balances between the two.*

- *I will record my evidence in the chart.*

- *To finish my writing, I need a concluding statement or paragraph.*

Topic: Functions of the Executive and Legislative branches of the U.S. government	
Main Point: The system of checks and balances maintains the balance of between the Executive and Legislative branches of the government.	**Details:** Each branch of government has certain powers. The system keeps one branch from gaining too much power over another.
Main Point: The president is the head of the Executive branch, which also includes the vice president and the cabinet.	**Details:** The executive branch applies the laws made by Congress. The president can propose new laws or veto laws he or she disagrees with. The president writes an operating budget for the country. The president can propose treaties.
Main Point: The Legislative branch includes the Senate and the House of Representatives, which make up Congress.	**Details:** Congress makes laws and controls federal spending. Congress must approve the president's budget and can require changes. Congress can override the president's vetoes and reject treaties.

Read and analyze the model. Distribute the student writing model and checklist on pages 32–33 to students. Read them aloud. Discuss with students whether or not the writer was successful at accomplishing this task. Ask them to complete the checklist as you discuss the informative/explanatory text.

COMMON CORE
STATE STANDARD
W.6.2

Read the passages.

Three Branches of Government

1.   Refers to the main divisions of the U.S. government. Each division, or branch, is granted certain powers that allow the government to function. The three branches work together to keep the country running smoothly. Additionally, a system of **checks and balances** keeps each branch from gaining power over the other two. The three branches of the U.S. government are the executive, legislative, and judicial.

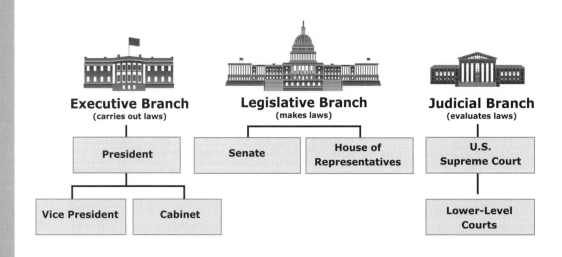

Executive Branch
(carries out laws)

Legislative Branch
(makes laws)

Judicial Branch
(evaluates laws)

| President | | Senate | House of Representatives | U.S. Supreme Court |

| Vice President | Cabinet | | Lower-Level Courts |

(continued)

Common Core Writing to Texts Grade 6 • ©2014 Newmark Learning, LLC

COMMON CORE
STATE STANDARD
W.6.2

(continued)

Executive Branch

2. The executive branch of government includes the **president**, the **vice president**, and the **cabinet**. The president and vice president are elected to their offices. Members of the cabinet are appointed by the president. The president's primary role is to act as the figurehead of government as well as commander-in-chief of the armed services. The vice president and the cabinet serve as advisers to the president. The executive branch is responsible for applying the laws of the land, setting up an operating budget for the country, appointing justices to the Supreme Court, and declaring a state of emergency during disasters, among other tasks.

Legislative Branch

3. The legislative branch of government includes two bodies that make laws: the **Senate** and the **House of Representatives**. Each body has its own set of responsibilities and tasks. Members are elected by popular vote. The legislative branch is collectively referred to as **Congress**. The role of Congress is to ensure that the will of the people is done. Congress makes laws, controls federal money, and approves (or denies) the budget submitted by the president. Congress also has the power to declare war.

Judicial Branch

4. The judicial branch of government includes the **U.S. Supreme Court** as well as **lower-level courts**. The judicial branch is responsible for overseeing the laws of the country. The Supreme Court reviews and interprets laws. It uses its power of **judicial review** to study whether laws are constitutional, or in keeping with the **U.S. Constitution**. The Supreme Court can use judicial review to study and weigh in on the acts of the executive branch, too.

(continue to next passage)

(continued)

Checks and Balances

1. The system of checks and balances is designed to balance power in a government. Checks and balances are used by governments that operate under a constitution, such as the United States. A constitutional government is usually broken into several parts, or branches. Each branch holds different powers. Checks and balances are activities between the different branches that keep any one branch from becoming more powerful than the others. In the United States, checks and balances maintain power among the executive, legislative, and judicial branches of government.

Checks and Balances
Between the Executive and Legislative Branches

2. The executive branch checks the power of the legislative branch in several ways. The president can propose laws for Congress to pass. The president can veto the laws that are passed by Congress. The president also must negotiate with Congress on an annual operating budget for the country.

3. The legislative branch, in turn, checks the power of the executive branch. Congress can override presidential vetoes. It can also reject treaties proposed by the president, as well as nominations of federal officials, including cabinet members and judges. The president must submit an annual operating budget to Congress, which can require changes to be made prior to approval. Finally, Congress can impeach and remove any president that it believes has broken the law or abused the powers of the office.

Checks and Balances
Between the Legislative and Judicial Branches

4. The legislative and judicial branches also check each other's powers. Congress can reject nominees to both the federal courts and the Supreme Court. Congress can impeach judges and remove them from the bench. Congress can also amend the U.S. Constitution to overturn decisions that have been made by the Supreme Court.

(continued)

(continued)

5. For its part, the Supreme Court uses the power of judicial review to review the actions of the legislative branch. Judicial review allows the Supreme Court to examine the laws passed by Congress. If necessary, the court can declare laws unconstitutional.

Checks and Balances
Between the Judicial and Executive Branches

6. The judicial branch also checks the executive branch through judicial review. The Supreme Court can review the president's actions to determine if they are constitutional. For example, the Supreme Court can examine and rule on treaties that the president makes with other countries.

7. Finally, the executive branch checks the power of the judicial branch. The president nominates the judges who sit on the U.S. Supreme Court and the lower federal courts. The president can overrule the judicial branch by pardoning convicted criminals or granting amnesty, which means forgiving a whole class of crime.

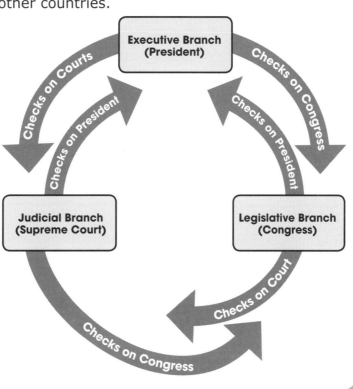

Read and analyze the prompt.

Informative/Explanatory Prompt

Using facts and details from both passages, explain the function of the Executive Branch and the Legislative Branch of the U.S. government and the checks and balances between the two.

COMMON CORE
STATE STANDARD
W.6.2

Read and analyze the model.

Checks and Balances in the Executive and Legislative Branches of the U.S. Government

By Elena Sanchez

The Executive and Legislative branches of the U.S. government must work together to perform their duties. For example, they must make laws and pass a budget. Each branch has certain functions that prevent the other from gaining too much power in the process. This is called checks and balances.

The president is the head of the executive branch, and the vice president and the cabinet serve as advisers. The president can propose new laws or veto laws with which he or she disagrees. The president also writes the operating budget for the country and may propose treaties with other countries. But Congress must approve all of them before the president signs the bills into law and must give final approval to the budget or treaties.

The legislative branch includes the Senate and the House of Representatives, which make up Congress. Congress writes bills, but the president must sign them before they become law. It also controls how federal money is spent and may ask for changes in the budget before it will give its approval. Then the budget goes to the president to be signed. If the president vetoes a law, Congress can override the veto. It can also reject treaties.

Because both branches of government have powers of approval and denial, neither one can pass a law or a budget all by itself. That ensures that neither one gets too powerful.

✔ Writing Checklist: Informative/Explanatory

- ❏ The writer started with a clear introduction to the topic.

- ❏ The writer grouped related information in paragraphs.

- ❏ The writer developed the topic with relevant facts, definitions, concrete details, quotations, or other information and examples from the texts.

- ❏ The writer used transition words and signal language to support the relationships among ideas.

- ❏ The writer used precise language and terminology to explain the topic.

- ❏ The writer used a formal voice.

- ❏ The writer wrote a conclusion related to the information he or she presented.

- ❏ The writer reviewed his or her writing for good grammar.

- ❏ The writer reviewed his or her writing for capitalization, punctuation, and spelling.

COMMON CORE
STATE STANDARD
W.6.3

Writing a Narrative

Mini-Lesson 5: **Writing to One Text**

> **COMMON CORE STATE STANDARD W.6.3**
>
> **Write narratives to develop real or imagined experiences or events using effective technique, relevant descriptive details, and well-structured event sequences.**
>
> a. Engage and orient the reader by establishing a context and introducing a narrator and/or characters; organize an event sequence that unfolds naturally and logically.
>
> b. Use narrative techniques, such as dialogue, pacing, and description, to develop experiences, events, and/or characters.
>
> c. Use a variety of transition words, phrases, and clauses to convey sequence and signal shifts from one time frame or setting to another.
>
> d. Use precise words and phrases, relevant descriptive details, and sensory language to convey experiences and events.
>
> e. Provide a conclusion that follows from the narrated experiences or events.

Explain to students that they will often encounter narrative writing prompts that instruct them to respond directly to a fiction passage they have read. Then take the following steps to guide students through the process of writing a narrative piece in response to one source.

Read the passage. Distribute pages 36–37 to students. Depending on students' needs, you may wish to read the passage aloud, have students read it with a partner, or have them read it independently.

Read and analyze the prompt. Read the prompt at the bottom of page 37 with students. Model how to analyze the prompt. Ask questions such as the following:

- *What form of writing does the prompt ask for?* (narrative)

- *How can you tell?* (The prompt asks me to rewrite a story from Dad's point of view.)

- *What is the purpose of the assignment?* (to write a story)

- *What information do I need to complete the task?* (I need to use evidence from the story "Striking a Chord.")

Plan the writing. Use page 124 to model how to plan writing a narrative. Draw the graphic organizer on the board, but do not fill in the answers. Work with students to fill in the organizer. You may wish to use the think-alouds and annotations as a guide.

- *The writing prompt asks me to rewrite the story "Striking a Chord" from Dad's point of view. I need to be sure that I tell what Dad thinks and how he feels.*

- *I will record the characters, setting, goal, major events, and ending/ resolution in the chart.*

Characters	Setting
a dad his son, Jimmy	guitar store home

Goal
Write the story from Dad's point of view, including his thoughts and feelings.

Major Events
1. Dad promises Jimmy he'll buy him a guitar if he does well in English. 2. Dad takes Jimmy to the music store to choose a guitar. 3. They have to choose a used guitar because the new ones are too expensive. 4. They choose an older red guitar that sounds fine. 5. Dad promises to give Jimmy lessons.

Ending/Resolution
Jimmy's guitar turns out to be his father's first guitar.

Read and analyze the model. Distribute the student writing model and checklist on pages 38–39 to students. Read them aloud. Discuss with students whether or not the writer was successful at accomplishing the task. Ask them to complete the checklist as you discuss the narrative.

COMMON CORE
STATE STANDARD

W.6.3

Read the passage below.

Striking a Chord

1.   Jimmy and his dad entered the music store, and without hesitating, Jimmy sprinted to the back of the store. He peered excitedly at all the different guitars hanging on the wall. Dad had promised Jimmy that if he did well in his English class, he would reward him by buying him a guitar, something Jimmy had always wanted. Well, Jimmy aced his class, so there they were in the music store.

2.   The new guitars were all too expensive, so Dad told Jimmy he would have to choose a used one. After Jimmy browsed through the selection of used guitars for a few minutes, Dad asked him which one he liked.

3.   "I don't know," Jimmy replied. "There are so many to choose from."

4.   Dad told Jimmy he could help him decide, and he picked up a black guitar. When he was just a young boy, Dad had learned to play guitar. He started strumming the guitar and then stopped abruptly.

5.   "This guitar isn't good for you," Dad said. "It's a little too difficult to play."

6.   Dad hung the guitar back up on the wall, grabbed another one, and started playing. Again, he quickly stopped.

7.   "This one is better, but it doesn't sound the greatest," Dad said.

8.   After replacing the instrument, Dad picked up an old yet stunning-looking red guitar. He strummed a few chords and began smiling. Handing off the guitar to Jimmy, he said, "I think this one would be perfect for you."

(continued)

(continued)

9.   Jimmy knew how to play only one guitar chord, which Dad had taught him in the past, so he played the chord a few times. He immediately loved the look and feel of the guitar and was impressed by its sound. Jimmy was sure this was the guitar for him. He told Dad he decided on the red guitar, and then Dad helped him pick out some accessories, including an instruction booklet.

10.   Jimmy couldn't wait to get home and play his guitar. He told Dad he would practice every day and learn as many chords as he could. Dad said he would teach Jimmy some guitar techniques, too.

11.   As he had promised, Jimmy practiced playing his guitar every day, using his instruction booklet, and Dad even gave him some lessons. Jimmy learned many new chords and was developing a true talent for the guitar.

12.   One day, Dad was giving a lesson when, suddenly, the red guitar seemed oddly familiar to him. Then he saw the worn initials and he knew what the connection was: It was the very guitar he had as a boy, before he traded it in at the music store for a new one. All these years later, the guitar had ended up in his son's hands.

Read and analyze the prompt.

Narrative Prompt

> **Rewrite the story "Striking a Chord" from Jimmy's father's point of view. Remember to include narrative techniques, such as dialogue and description. Use details from the story you have already read to inform your new narrative.**

COMMON CORE
STATE STANDARD
W.6.3

Read and analyze the model.

A Guitar Worth Keeping

By Adam Cappucci

Jimmy was trying so hard in school that I thought he deserved a reward. He had wanted a guitar for a long time. I wished I could just take him to the store and let him pick one, because I myself love to play and have since I was about his age. But Jimmy was having a hard time getting motivated to do his English homework, so I told him that if he did well in the class, I'd buy him that guitar.

The months went by and I put a little money aside each week. Jimmy did a great job on his homework and got his first A on an essay. When he brought home his report card, I was proud to see that his English grade was up to a B plus. I let him squirm for a minute, as though maybe I'd forgotten my promise, but then I said, "Let's go." We raced to my truck.

When we got to the music store, Jimmy headed straight for the shiny, new guitars. I looked at a couple of the price tags. "Jimmy," I said, "these are too expensive. Let's check out the used models."

He tried out a couple he liked the looks of, but one was too hard for a beginner to play and I wasn't happy with the sound of the other one. Then I picked up a beautiful red guitar and strummed it a few times. Jimmy loved it. The guitar was old, but it sounded as pretty as it looked. I was almost afraid to look at the price, but it was fine.

(continued)

(continued)

It turned out Jimmy liked it the best, too. So then I said, "Why don't you pick out a shoulder strap, Jim, and I'll find you an instruction book." We were two happy guys when we left the store.

Jimmy promised to practice every day, and I hoped he would. I really think he's got talent. He's learned some chords from the book we got, and I get out my guitar sometimes and show him some techniques.

One day when we were playing together, I took his guitar to show him how to hold his fingers for a chord. Suddenly, something about the instrument felt really familiar. I looked it over carefully, until I found the tiny, worn initials scratched into the back of the neck. My initials. It took me a minute to start breathing again, and then I said, "Jimmy, this was my first guitar. I loved it more than anything, but I traded it in for a new one because I couldn't have both." As hard as it is to believe, after all these years, my guitar had ended up in my own son's hands.

✔ Writing Checklist: Narrative

- ❏ The writer established a setting or situation for his or her narrative.
- ❏ The writer introduced a narrator and/or characters.
- ❏ The writer organized the narrative into a sequence of unfolding events.
- ❏ The writer used dialogue and description to develop events and show how characters respond to them.
- ❏ The writer used transitional words to show the sequence of events.
- ❏ The writer used concrete words and phrases and sensory details to describe events.
- ❏ The writer wrote a conclusion to the events in his or her narrative.
- ❏ The writer reviewed his or her writing for good grammar.
- ❏ The writer reviewed his or her writing for capitalization, punctuation, and spelling.

COMMON CORE
STATE STANDARD
W.6.3

Writing a Narrative

Mini-Lesson 6: Writing to Multiple Texts

> **COMMON CORE STATE STANDARD W.6.3**
>
> **Write narratives to develop real or imagined experiences or events using effective technique, relevant descriptive details, and well-structured event sequences.**
>
> a. Engage and orient the reader by establishing a context and introducing a narrator and/or characters; organize an event sequence that unfolds naturally and logically.
>
> b. Use narrative techniques, such as dialogue, pacing, and description, to develop experiences, events, and/or characters.
>
> c. Use a variety of transition words, phrases, and clauses to convey sequence and signal shifts from one time frame or setting to another.
>
> d. Use precise words and phrases, relevant descriptive details, and sensory language to convey experiences and events.
>
> e. Provide a conclusion that follows from the narrated experiences or events.

Explain to students that they will often encounter writing prompts that instruct them to respond directly to more than one passage. For example, they might have to read two fictional passages by the same author, two fictional passages with a similar theme, or two informational passages about the same topic. Then take the following steps to guide students through the process of writing a narrative piece in response to multiple texts.

Read the passages. Distribute pages 42–45 to students. Depending on students' needs, you may wish to read the passages aloud, have students read them with a partner, or have them read the passages independently.

Read and analyze the prompt. Read the prompt at the bottom of page 45 with students. Model how to analyze the prompt. Ask questions such as the following:

- *What form of writing does the prompt ask for?* (narrative)

- *How can you tell?* (The prompt asks me to write a sequel to the story.)

- *What is the purpose of the assignment?* (to write a story that shows the two main characters meeting)

- *What information do I need to complete the task?* (I need to use evidence from the story "Reggie's Lie" and the play "The Missing Chameleon.")

Plan the writing. Draw the following graphic organizer on the board. You may also wish to distribute the matching graphic organizer located on page 125. Use the following think-alouds to model how to complete the graphic organizer. Ask for student input as you fill in the chart on the board.

- *The prompt asks me to write a story in which Reggie and Marco meet and discuss their experiences and the lesson they both learned.*

- *The prompt also asks me to use dialogue in my story.*

- *At the end of my story, the characters should resolve never to lie again.*

Characters:	**Setting:**
Reggie Marco Douglas Chris	basketball court at a neighborhood playground

Details from Stories I Read	**Events**
Reggie lies about having written a poem, and his grandfather shows him how embarrassing it can be when your lie spreads to others. Marco lies about who left the chameleon's cage door open and confesses only when his whole class is to be punished. Both have learned their lessons and don't lie anymore.	Douglas has a new basketball he says he got for his birthday. His friends don't believe it's his, but they all play with the basketball. The rightful owner shows up looking for his ball.

Problem:

Douglas seems to be planning to keep a basketball that isn't his. Reggie and Marco both know from experience that lies can get out of control and it's better to not lie.

Resolution:

Reggie and Marco tell their stories and Douglas decides to do the right thing based on his friends' experiences with lying.

Read and analyze the model. Distribute the student writing model and checklist on pages 46–47 to students. Read them aloud. Discuss with students whether or not the writer was successful at accomplishing this task. Ask them to complete the checklist as you discuss the narrative piece.

COMMON CORE
STATE STANDARD
W.6.3

Read the passages.

Reggie's Lie

1. Tomorrow would be Reggie Lyons's first opportunity to see his grandfather since Grandpa moved from his farmhouse in the country to a nursing home in the city. Reggie planned to spend the entire day with Grandpa, and he wanted their visit to be extra-special. So he decided to make Grandpa a heartfelt gift. Reggie took his sketch pad from art class and drew a pencil sketch of a photograph of Grandpa and him taken about six years earlier. The finished sketch showed Grandpa pushing five-year-old Reggie on a swing that hung from the birch tree in front of Grandpa's farmhouse.

2. As Reggie studied the sketch, he thought it lacked something. He knew Grandpa liked poetry, so he thumbed through a book of poems. A poem about boys swinging on birch trees caught Reggie's eye, so he copied the verse onto the sketch in beautiful script.

3. The next day, Reggie's parents took him to Field Crest Nursing Home, and Reggie found Grandpa in the community room. He plucked the sketch from his backpack and handed it to Grandpa. Grandpa surveyed the drawing and took his time reading the poem.

4. "What a beautiful drawing," he said, "and what beautiful lines of poetry. Did you write this poem yourself?"

5. "I did," Reggie fibbed.

6. Grandpa's eyes clouded over for a second, but then he smiled again. "It's truly remarkable," he said and then called to a woman across the room. "Doris, come listen to this poem my grandson wrote."

7. Blushing, Reggie tried to hide beneath his cap as Grandpa read the poem and Doris gushed and squealed. As more folks came closer to listen, Reggie squirmed in his seat.

8. For the rest of the afternoon, Reggie couldn't meet Grandpa's eye or concentrate as they played chess. Shame and guilt festered inside him, ruining his special day with Grandpa. Finally, when they returned to Grandpa's room after dinner, Reggie broke down.

(continued)

Common Core Writing to Texts Grade 6 • ©2014 Newmark Learning, LLC

(continued)

9. "Grandpa," said Reggie, looking at his feet, "I copied that poem from a book of poetry at my house."

10. Grandpa gently placed his hand under Reggie's chin and made the boy look him in the eyes. "I know, Reggie," said Grandpa. "That poem is by Robert Frost and has always been one of my favorites."

11. Reggie's eyes widened. "You knew? Why didn't you say anything? How come you told your friends to listen to the poem?" he asked.

12. "Because I wanted to show you that lies spread like wildfire, Reggie," Grandpa said.

13. "That little fib ruined today," said Reggie, "and I couldn't leave here without coming clean. I never want to feel that way again. I'm so sorry."

14. Grandpa gave Reggie a hug. "You're forgiven," said Grandpa, "but now that your conscience is clear, how about a rematch on that chess game?"

15. "You're on," said Reggie.

(continue to next passage)

(continued)

The Missing Chameleon

1. *Setting: A classroom filled with desks. At center stage sits an empty lizard tank with an open door, and two students, STEPHANIE and MARCO, stand near the tank with worried expressions on their faces.*

2. **STEPHANIE:** Mrs. Miller's going to be furious if she discovers that you left Rainbow's tank open and allowed him to escape, Marco.

3. *(Marco nods as Mrs. Miller, the teacher, enters the room.)*

4. **MRS. MILLER:** Stephanie, Marco, shouldn't you be in art class?

5. **MARCO:** Yes, Mrs. Miller, but I came to check on Rainbow, and I have some terrible news—someone left his tank open, and he's missing.

6. **MRS. MILLER:** *(with raised eyebrows)* Do you know who left the tank open?

7. **MARCO:** *(shaking his head)* No, ma'am. I fed Rainbow before lunch, and I know I closed the tank before leaving the room.

8. **MRS. MILLER:** *(turning to Stephanie)* Stephanie?

9. **STEPHANIE:** *(glancing at Marco, then shaking her head)* No, ma'am.

10. **MRS. MILLER:** *(looking between the two)* Well, since you two are here, please help me locate Rainbow. Looking for a small chameleon in a large classroom is like looking for a needle in a haystack.

11. *(Stephanie, Marco, and Mrs. Miller begin looking inside desks and behind bookshelves. Other students enter the room and take their seats, and Mrs. Miller stops searching to address them.)*

12. **MRS. MILLER:** Class, I've been informed that someone left Rainbow's tank open and now he's missing. If you are the person responsible for this, please step forward.

13. *(Mrs. Miller surveys the class as the students quietly murmur and look at one another, but no one steps forward.)*

(continued)

(continued)

14. **MRS. MILLER:** *(crossing her arms)* Until someone steps forward to claim responsibility, I have no choice but to punish the entire class. Please write your vocabulary words twenty times each.

15. *(Groaning, the students grumpily remove notebooks from their desks and begin to write. Marco glances around at his angry classmates and finally stands.)*

16. **MARCO:** *(staring at his feet)* I left the tank open and allowed Rainbow to escape, Mrs. Miller. I didn't tell you the truth because I was afraid of getting in trouble, but it's not fair to punish others for my mistake.

17. **STEPHANIE:** *(standing)* I apologize for lying, too, Mrs. Miller. I knew Marco left the tank open, but I didn't want him to get into trouble.

18. **MRS. MILLER:** *(sternly)* You shouldn't have lied . . . *(more gently)* but I appreciate your honesty. *(Opening her desk drawer, she removes a much smaller tank containing Rainbow, and Marco's eyes and mouth open wide.)* Marco, I realized shortly after you left for lunch that you left the tank door open—for the third time—and I wanted to teach you a lesson in responsibility. *(smiling)* It seems you've learned another important lesson, as well.

19. **MARCO:** *(sheepishly)* Yes, Mrs. Miller. I promise to be more responsible AND to always tell the truth.

Read and analyze the prompt.

Narrative Prompt

> **Write a sequel story in which Reggie of "Reggie's Lie" and Marco of "The Missing Chameleon" meet. Have them discuss their experiences and the lesson they have both learned. Use dialogue in your story. At the end of the story, they should resolve never to lie again.**

Read and analyze the model.

Two on One

By Glenn Dunlap

Reggie and Marco wandered onto the basketball court to shoot some baskets. Douglas, whom they knew from school, was already there. He had a brand-new basketball that he was dribbling back and forth on the court, stopping to shoot once in a while.

"Hey, Douglas," shouted Marco. "Where'd you get the new ball?"

"I got it for my birthday," said Douglas. "My grandmother gave it to me."

"Your birthday was last summer," objected Reggie. "How come we're just seeing this ball now?"

"Oh, I didn't want to get it all dirty and stuff," said Douglas. "And I was afraid I might lose it. Besides, my mother said I had to keep it at home."

"What good would that do you?" asked Marco. "You don't have a hoop in your yard."

"I don't know. That's what she said. Are we going to play or not?" Douglas muttered angrily.

"Okay, okay," said the other boys.

They put Marco's old ball aside and started to play. Whoever had the ball tried to score and the other two tried to block him. It was more fun playing with a new ball that bounced well and was easy to see, with its bright orange surface. They played hard, and after 20 minutes they decided to sit down and rest.

As they sat in the cool shade, Reggie asked Douglas, "Whose ball is that really?"

"It's mine, I told you," he snapped, tucking the ball behind him, out of sight.

Reggie looked at Marco. Marco didn't believe Douglas, either.

(continued)

Common Core Writing to Texts Grade 6 • ©2014 Newmark Learning, LLC

(continued)

"You know," said Reggie, "One time I tried to pass off a Robert Frost poem as my own work. My grandpa knew I didn't write it, but he called over a bunch of people to read it and said, 'Listen to the poem my grandson wrote.' I was so embarrassed I couldn't look anyone in the eye. Later I told Grandpa the truth, and he forgave me, because he knew I had learned my lesson. I never lie anymore. It's not worth it."

"Yeah," said Marco. "I did that once. I told Mrs. Miller it wasn't me that left the tank door open when the chameleon got out. She decided to punish the whole class because no one would admit it. Then I told her the truth. She knew it was me all along, because she went into the classroom right after I left from feeding Rainbow. And Rainbow was safe in another tank in her desk. Everybody was really mad at me for causing them trouble for nothing. No, it definitely isn't worth it."

Just then, another boy walked across the street and onto the court. Seeing the three boys sitting in the shade, he asked, "Did you guys see a basketball here? I think I left mine by mistake. It was brand new."

Reggie and Marco looked at Douglas. He smiled. "Yeah, man," he said, rolling the ball from behind him. "Here it is. We played with it a little. I hope you don't mind."

"No, that's okay," said the boy. "I'm just glad to get it back. I'm Chris. Do you guys want to play some two-on-two?"

✔ Writing Checklist: Narrative

- ❑ The writer established a setting or situation for his narrative.
- ❑ The writer introduced a narrator and/or characters.
- ❑ The writer organized his narrative into a sequence of unfolding events.
- ❑ The writer used dialogue and description to develop events and show how characters respond to them.
- ❑ The writer used transitional words to show his sequence of events.
- ❑ The writer used concrete words and phrases and sensory details to describe events.
- ❑ The writer wrote a conclusion to the events in his narrative.
- ❑ The writer reviewed his writing for good grammar.
- ❑ The writer reviewed his writing for capitalization, punctuation, and spelling.

Practice Texts with Prompts

How to Use Practice Texts with Prompts

This section of Writing to Texts provides opportunities for students to practice writing frequently in a wide range of genres and provides authentic practice for standardized writing assessments. Each practice lesson contains a passage or pair of passages followed by three prompts.

Before beginning, assign students one of the prompts, or ask them each to choose one. Explain to students that they are to plan and write an essay about the passage or passages according to the instructions in the chosen prompt. They should write on a separate piece of paper, or in a writing journal designated for writing practice.

There are various ways to use the practice section. You may wish to have students complete the writing tasks at independent workstations, as homework assignments, or as test practice in a timed environment.

If you choose to use these as practice for standardized tests, assign one prompt and give students 60 minutes to execute the task. In using these as test practice, tell students that they should think of their writing as a draft, and tell them they will not have additional time to revise their work.

You may also choose to have students respond to the prompts orally to strengthen academic oral language skills.

Graphic organizers for each type of writing are included on pages 120–125. You may choose to distribute them to help students plan and organize. On pages 126–127, reproducible Student Writing Checklists are provided. Distribute them to students to serve as checklists as they write, or as self-assessment guides.

Conducting Research

The Common Core State Standards require that students are provided opportunities to learn research techniques and to apply these skills in their preparation of projects. The passages in this section can make for research project starters. After students respond to an informational prompt, ask them to conduct further research on information from the practice text in order to build their knowledge.

Explain to students that researchers take good notes, connect new knowledge to what is already known, organize information into sensible layouts for a report, cite their sources, and use their own words to convey the information.

Tell students to gather information from print and digital sources. Have them take brief notes on sources and sort their facts, details, and evidence into categories. They may choose an appropriate organizer from pages 120–125.

Practice Texts with Prompts Table of Contents

COMMON CORE
STATE STANDARDS

W.6.1–
W.6.10

Name_____ Date_____

Read the passage below.

Peculiar Pancakes

Scene 1 – The Kitchen

1. *(Brothers Ralph and Randy and their father are at the kitchen table. Eleven-year-old Ralph is hungry and is gobbling his food while five-year-old Randy just stares at his plate.)*

2. **Dad:** Ralph, slow down or you'll get a stomachache. Randy, what's the matter?

3. **Randy:** I'm not hungry, and I don't like any of this food.

4. **Ralph:** If those were pancakes, he'd be eating them all—and ours, too!

5. **Dad:** You know, Randy, you really have to eat a variety of good food to be healthy, and everything on that plate is good for you.

6. **Ralph:** Yeah, Randy, look at all the good food—mashed potatoes, peas, carrots . . .

7. *(Randy continues to stare at his plate.)*

8. *(Later, Ralph is helping Dad wash the dishes while Randy is playing in another room.)*

9. **Dad:** I don't know what to do about Randy. He's such a picky eater. All he wants to eat are pancakes—for breakfast, lunch, and dinner. Pancakes are okay sometimes, but he can't eat them for every meal!

10. **Ralph:** Let me think about this, Dad. I'll try to figure out a way to get him eat something else.

Scene 2 – The Cafeteria

11. *(Ralph is sitting at the school cafeteria with his friends Jeff and Steven.)*

12. **Ralph:** I'm trying to help my dad think of a plan. My little

(continued)

Common Core Writing to Texts Grade 6 • ©2014 Newmark Learning, LLC

Name_____ Date_____

(continued)

brother refuses to eat anything but pancakes, and if he keeps this up, he's going to turn into one giant pancake!

13. (*Jeff and Steven laugh at the mental image of Randy as a pancake.*)

14. **Jeff:** Maybe you can invent a new food besides pancakes that he will actually like.

15. **Ralph:** It would take a chef, a farmer, or a scientist to invent a new food.

16. **Steven:** My aunt is a chef who likes to make some strange new creations. She said that most new food inventions are just combinations of normal foods.

17. **Ralph:** That makes sense, but we can't combine just anything. What if you mixed tuna in your breakfast cereal, or peanut butter in your soup?

18. (*The boys laugh at these unusual dishes, and Jeff accidentally bumps the table, spilling the food on their trays and knocking carrots and peas into Steven's mashed potatoes. Their teacher, Mr. Lamont, comes over.*)

19. **Mr. Lamont:** Settle down there, guys. It's bad manners to play with your food.

20. **Ralph:** We're not playing, Mr. Lamont. We're experimenting, and I think we just came up with something great!

21. **Steven:** What are you talking about?

22. **Ralph:** Look what happened here. If we put carrot shreds and peas in mashed potatoes and then bake them in a pan, you get pancakes. They'd be healthy and probably delicious. I bet my little brother would eat them.

23. **Mr. Lamont:** I think you might be on to something there, Ralph.

24. **Ralph:** I think Randy will love these. Maybe I'll even start a business—"Peculiar Pancakes"!

COMMON CORE
STATE STANDARDS
W.6.1–
W.6.10

Name_____ Date_____

Argument Prompt

Do you think Randy will like pancakes made of carrot shreds, peas, and mashed potatoes? Why or why not? Use details from the text to support your opinion.

Informative/Explanatory Prompt

What can you tell about Ralph from the play? What kind of person is he? Support your explanation with details from the text.

Narrative Prompt

Write a sequel to the play in which Ralph and Dad make peculiar pancakes for Randy. Use details from the original play to make a smooth transition to the sequel.

Common Core
State Standards
W.6.1–
W.6.10

Name_____ Date_____

Read the passage below.

The Moon Landing

1.   Janet Meriwether and her family had just returned home from shopping and Sunday dinner. Janet had felt hot and sticky all day, so she poured herself some iced tea, plopped on the porch swing, and gently tapped her toe on the concrete to set the swing in motion. Around her, moisture hung in the hot, still, July air like damp laundry. Janet sipped her iced tea and pressed the cold glass against her forehead.

2.   Just then, the screen door burst open and Janet's four-year-old brother James appeared on the porch. "Janet, quick, come see! A spaceship is landing on the MOON!" he cried. He retreated into the house, and Janet heard his tiny feet thudding down the hallway.

3.   Curious, Janet followed James inside. Her parents and her older sister Jennifer had already gathered around the small television set in the living room. The screen displayed grainy, black-and-white images of the moon's surface. Janet's family sat in silence as the spaceship descended ever closer to the moon, and Janet felt a twinge of anxiety as a detailed view of the moon's craters appeared. The news correspondents stopped talking, and Janet held her breath. The only sounds were the steady, calm voices of the astronauts aboard the spaceship. Suddenly, the spaceship touched down and came to a stop, and the screen went dark for a moment. The voice of Neil Armstrong, one of the astronauts, broadcast loud and clear: "The Eagle has landed."

4.   At that moment, 4:18 P.M. on July 20, 1969, the entire Meriwether family breathed a collective sigh of relief. James clapped and cheered, and Janet's mother hugged her father.

(continued)

COMMON CORE
STATE STANDARDS
W.6.1–
W.6.10

Name_____ Date_____

(continued)

5.   Janet continued watching the news for much of the evening but eventually drifted to sleep on the couch. The next thing she knew, Mr. Meriwether shook her awake. "Janet, honey, you don't want to miss this."

6.   Looking around, Janet rubbed her eyes. James, who had fallen asleep long before Janet, now appeared wide awake with his eyes glued to the television. Janet followed his gaze and perked up when she realized that Neil Armstrong stood on a contraption outside the spaceship. He looked enormous in his bulky space suit and large, round helmet. A caption at the bottom of the television screen read, "LIVE FROM THE SURFACE OF THE MOON."

7.   It seemed as if an eternity passed, and then, just a few minutes before 11:00 P.M., Neil Armstrong stepped onto the moon, the first human ever to do so. He spoke, his voice slightly muffled by static: "That's one small step for man, one giant leap for mankind."

8.   Soon, Buzz Aldrin joined Neil Armstrong on the moon. Goose bumps appeared on Janet's skin as she observed the astronauts erect a flag and bounce around the moon's surface.

9.   "Kids," said Mrs. Meriwether with tears in her eyes, "you have just witnessed history."

Name_____ Date_____

COMMON CORE
STATE STANDARDS
W.6.1–
W.6.10

Argument Prompt

How do you think Janet and her family feel about the spaceship landing on the moon? Use details from the text to support your opinion.

Informative/Explanatory Prompt

The text quotes Neil Armstrong as saying "That's one small step for man, one giant leap for mankind." Explain the meaning of this statement using details from the text.

Narrative Prompt

Write a journal entry Neil Armstrong might have recorded about his experience that day.

COMMON CORE
STATE STANDARDS
W.6.1–
W.6.10

Name_____ Date_____

Read the passage below.

For Everything a Season
(An Ancient Greek Myth)

1. Demeter was the sister of Zeus and the goddess of all growing things on Earth. It was Demeter's care that gave bright, beautiful flowers to the meadows, sparkling leaves to the trees, and soft grass to the soil underfoot. It was Demeter who made sure that the sun shone, the crops were plentiful, and the people had enough to eat.

2. Demeter had a daughter, Persephone. Demeter loved Persephone beyond everything. Persephone was a lovely, spirited, and carefree girl. All who saw her were enchanted by her beauty and kindness.

3. Even Hades, the dark god of the underworld, could not tear his eyes from her once he came upon her deep within the woods. He wanted her loveliness all to himself. But Hades knew that Persephone would never agree to leave the sunny Earth. Desperate, he seized her, and carried her off to the underworld, far beyond her mother's reach.

4. When Demeter realized that her daughter was missing, she searched and searched for her. She became enraged and filled with grief. She stopped caring for Earth. The flowers halted their upward march. The trees began to shed their leaves. The grass turned brown. The sun hid behind the clouds, afraid to show his face. But Demeter did not care. She cared only about finding her daughter.

5. Soon Zeus became afraid that Demeter would never stop grieving and that all the people on Earth would starve. He forced Hades to release Persephone.

(continued)

Common Core Writing to Texts Grade 6 • ©2014 Newmark Learning, LLC

COMMON CORE
STATE STANDARDS
W.6.1–
W.6.10

Name_____ Date_____

(continued)

6.   Hades pretended to agree, but played one last trick. As Persephone began her journey from the underworld, he gave her a juicy, red pomegranate. Hades knew that if someone ate food from the underworld, he or she would be forced to stay there.

7.   When Persephone ate the pomegranate, she sealed her fate. Although she would be able to spend a part of each year above ground in the sun with her mother, she would also have to return to the underworld to spend part of the year with Hades.

8.   Every year thereafter, Demeter fell into sadness as Persephone descended to the underworld. While Demeter grieved, Earth grieved with her. Through the long winter months, the sun hardly dared to show his face, and all growing things stayed hidden deep within Earth.

9.   However, each year when Hades released Persephone, Demeter was filled with joy. She rejoiced, and so did Earth. Each spring, Earth was overrun by the warm air, growing things, and happiness.

COMMON CORE
STATE STANDARDS
W.6.1–
W.6.10

Name_____ Date_____

Argument Prompt

Based on the myth, what do you think would have happened on Earth if Persephone refused to eat the pomegranate? Support your opinion with details from the text.

Informative/Explanatory Prompt

Using specific details from the myth, summarize the reason people on Earth experience winter.

Narrative Prompt

Rewrite the story from Demeter's point of view. Include her feelings about what happens to her and to Persephone.

Name_____ Date_____

Read the passage below.

Finders Keepers?

1.   The sun shone brightly overhead as Daniel and Brian raced to the top of the hill. Even though he was riding what he jokingly called his "model-T Ford," Daniel managed to reach the gate seconds before Brian. Bouncing on his thinning old tires, Daniel shouted "WHOOHOO! And the winner is . . . once again . . . ME!"

2.   Brian laughed as he glided to a stop. He didn't begrudge his friend the win. He smiled to himself as he thought that he might even have slowed down just a tiny bit to make it happen. He knew how badly Daniel felt about riding that old tin can, especially when riding next to Brian's slick yellow model that gleamed like gold in the sunshine. Daniel was his best friend. Anyway, he thought, he'll earn enough money for that new bike soon, and then we'll have some REAL races!

3.   "Ready to shoot some hoops, Dan?" he asked his friend.

4.   Daniel, however, wasn't paying attention. Instead, he was looking intently down at the grass near the gate. He glided over to a small brown lump of dirt. Reaching down, he picked the lump up and began brushing off dirt and grass.

5.   Brian came up behind him. "What's that?"

6.   "I think . . . it's someone's wallet." Daniel replied. As he turned it over in his hands, the two leather halves unfolded. With a quick, guilty look around, Daniel saw what was inside. He recognized the bright blue banner of a library card sticking out of a slot. He also saw a movie stub and what looked like a receipt from the local grocery store.

(continued)

COMMON CORE
STATE STANDARDS
W.6.1–
W.6.10

Name_____ Date_____

(continued)

7. He slid his fingers slowly into the back compartment. His eyes widened as he pulled out the edges of several neatly folded bills. He slid his finger between them. Not just any bills—twenty-dollar bills. The wallet contained three crisp, new twenty-dollar bills.

8. He heard Brian suck in his breath at his side.

9. Daniel looked up with confused eyes. "I think I just found sixty dollars." He swallowed hard. "I guess . . . I guess we should look for the person who dropped this."

10. "What, are you kidding me? Isn't that exactly how much you need for the bike?" asked Brian incredulously.

11. "Well, yeah. But . . ."

12. "Seriously?" Brian looked around the deserted park. "Because I don't see anyone standing here. I'm thinking this might be fate. I'm thinking this might be a case of finders keepers."

13. Daniel looked at Brian for a minute, hesitating. Then he seemed to come to a decision. He stuffed the wallet decisively into his backpack. His rusty bike wheels squealed as he turned his bike around.

14. "Where are you going?" Brian asked.

15. "Home," Daniel replied. "I want to talk to my dad. He helped that lady find her lost ring last summer. He will know how to help me."

16. "What, you mean he can help by driving you to the bike shop?" laughed Brian.

17. Daniel looked at his friend. "Yeah . . . um, yeah. Something like that." He started pedaling his trusty old "model-T" down the hill.

Common Core Writing to Texts Grade 6 • ©2014 Newmark Learning, LLC

Name_____ Date_____

COMMON CORE
STATE STANDARDS
W.6.1–
W.6.10

Argument Prompt

What do you think Daniel will do with the money in the wallet? Support your opinion with details from the text.

Informative/Explanatory Prompt

Why is Brian happy when Daniel beats him in a bike race? Support your explanation with details from the text.

Narrative Prompt

Write a sequel to the story in which Daniel discusses his problem with his father. Use details from "Finders Keepers?" to make a smooth transition to the sequel.

COMMON CORE
STATE STANDARDS
W.6.1–
W.6.10

Name_____ Date_____

Read the passage below.

The Lying Cow
Based on a West African folktale

1. Long ago, in a dry and barren region, there lived an old farmer. This old farmer had three sons: Chima, Kobina, and Enyin. The old farmer was not proud of his sons, nor was he kind to them. He only ever addressed them to complain about their work or to label them as lazy. He did not give them enough affection to fill a thimble!

2. Instead, the old farmer gave his affection to his favorite cow. The old farmer constantly praised the cow, saying, "This cow gives milk, pulls a plow, and bears calves each year. She is quiet, humble, hardworking, and productive. She is everything my sons are not!"

3. The cow would just quietly listen and smile smugly. She liked to be praised while the sons were being belittled.

4. One day, the old farmer told Chima to bring the cow to the watering hole for a drink. Chima dutifully led the cow to the watering hole and waited while she drank enough cool, fresh water for the whole morning.

5. But when they returned, the cow told the old farmer, "Your lazy son took me to a little mud puddle with no good water!" The old farmer was so angry he made Chima leave the farm.

6. The next day, the old farmer told Kobina to bring the cow to a good field for grazing. Kobina brought the cow to the best patch of green grass and gave her plenty of time to eat.

7. But when they returned, she lied again. "This lazy son gave me a handful of dead leaves to eat and nothing else!" The old farmer was so upset he forced Kobina to leave as well.

(continued)

                    Common Core Writing to Texts Grade 6 • ©2014 Newmark Learning, LLC

Name_____ Date_____

COMMON CORE
STATE STANDARDS
W.6.1–
W.6.10

(continued)

8.   The following day, the old farmer told Enyin to bring the cow to the lake for a bath. Enyin led the cow to the lake and carefully scrubbed her clean.

9.   But when they returned, the cow lied yet again. "This last lazy son left me alone to wash myself while he took a nap!" The old farmer was so annoyed he forced Enyin to leave, too.

10.   The day after that, the cow was standing in the yard looking for grass. She was thirsty, too, since the sun was hot. She tried rolling in the dirt to keep the flies away, but that only made her feel grimy. "Where is my water, grass, and bath?" she demanded.

11.   The old farmer came out and said, "My sons are gone now, and unfortunately I am too old to care for you properly. We will have to do without."

12.   The cow realized that her lying had ruined everything. She admitted her trickery and begged forgiveness. The old farmer realized he had been wrong about his sons all along. Immediately he sent for them and apologized for his ignorant behavior. They accepted his apology and soon the farm was running smoothly again.

COMMON CORE
STATE STANDARDS
W.6.1–
W.6.10

Name_____ Date_____

Argument Prompt

Do you think the farmer's sons are lazy? Why or why not? Use details from the text to support your opinion.

Informative/Explanatory Prompt

Explain how the author uses personification, giving human qualities to animals or objects, to add interest to the story. Provide specific examples and quotations from the text to support your explanation.

Narrative Prompt

Rewrite the story from the cow's point of view. What does she do? How does she feel at the end of the story?

Name_____ Date_____

COMMON CORE
STATE STANDARDS
W.6.1–
W.6.10

Read the passage below.

Earth—An Oblate Spheroid?

1.   The ancient Greeks were the first to figure out that Earth was not flat. They believed that Earth was round, a conclusion that appeared to be accurate.

2.   Thousands of years later, photos that astronauts took in space showed a spherical Earth. They gave Earth the nickname "Blue Marble" because of its shape. Appearances can be deceiving, however. Earth is not perfectly round as many are led to believe. Our planet is actually a bumpy spheroid and its shape is constantly changing.

3.   Isaac Newton first suggested that Earth's shape was not perfectly round. He believed our planet was shaped like an "oblate spheroid."

4.   This meant that Earth's shape was inflated at the equator. Modern geologists later confirmed that this was true. Earth was a bit deformed and bulged out 21 kilometers (13 miles) more at the equator than at the poles.

5.   Earth's shape also constantly changes over time. Mountains and valleys appear and disappear because of plate tectonics, which shift Earth's surface. Meteors sometimes hit Earth and create craters in its surface.

Traditional Globe   **Oblate Spheroid**

(continued)

Name_____ Date_____

(continued)

6. Earth's shape is also affected by what are called Earth tides. Much like ocean tides, earth tides are slight bulges in Earth's surface. Earth tides contribute to Earth's deformation only slightly, however.

7. Scientists are now trying to keep track of Earth's changing shape using thousands of global positioning system receivers. These receivers can detect even the slightest changes in the elevation of Earth's surface.

8. Another technique involves listening to radio waves in outer space to pick up any changes in the positions of the radio stations on the ground.

9. A different approach uses lasers to cover Earth's surface. Any tectonic shifts within the planet are detected by these lasers and provide a better idea of how Earth is being shaped. There are many methods that give people a better idea of Earth's true shape.

Name_____ Date_____

COMMON CORE
STATE STANDARDS
W.6.1–
W.6.10

Argument Prompt

Why do you think people think that Earth is perfectly round? Support your opinion with details from the text.

Informative/Explanatory Prompt

What is an oblate spheroid? Use details from the text to support your explanation.

Narrative Prompt

Write a story about a science teacher who is teaching her students that Earth is not perfectly round and how scientists keep track of Earth's changing shape. Base her lesson on the information in the text. Give the characters in your story names and use dialogue.

COMMON CORE
STATE STANDARDS
W.6.1–
W.6.10

Name_____ Date_____

Read the passage below.

Garrett Morgan

1. Garrett Morgan was born in Kentucky in 1877. His mother and father were former slaves. Despite his humble upbringing, Morgan went on to become one of America's most prominent inventors. He invented a lifesaving gas mask for firefighters and even built the first model for the modern traffic light. Morgan's inventions were very practical and helped others.

2. Morgan had a very mechanical mind. Even though he had only a sixth-grade education, he quickly learned how machines worked. He worked at a textile factory when he was young and was the only African American to work as a machine adjuster at the factory.

3. Morgan also had a mind for business. Learning all he could while working at the factory, he decided to open his own repair shop in Cleveland, Ohio, in 1907.

4. Morgan's shop thrived during a time when Americans had little money to spend. He opened a clothing business soon after and this was successful, too. Morgan soon became wealthy enough to purchase a car; he was the first African American in Cleveland to do so.

5. As a young man, Morgan noticed how difficult it was for firefighters to avoid the dangerous smoke in burning buildings. Their struggle inspired him to invent the first fire-safety hood, or gas mask. He designed the mask as a canvas hood with two tubes attached to it. The tubes filtered the smoke out of the hood and cooled the air inside. The safety hood allowed the wearer to breathe in a smoke-filled room.

6. Morgan's hood was a huge success. Soon it was being

(continued)

Common Core Writing to Texts Grade 6 • ©2014 Newmark Learning, LLC

Name_____ Date_____

COMMON CORE
STATE STANDARDS
W.6.1–
W.6.10

(continued)

used in more than 500 cities across the nation. It was also used by the U.S. Navy and the Army during World War I.

7.   The hood received even more positive exposure in 1916 when Morgan used it to rescue workers who had become trapped in a tunnel beneath Lake Erie after an explosion. The event made headlines and Morgan's bravery made him a hero.

8.   Morgan followed the success of his safety hood with another practical invention—a mechanical traffic light. His traffic light was unique because it included a third, cautionary signal between the stop and go signals. He patented the light in 1923 and sold it to General Electric. It became a widely used device for controlling road traffic.

9.   Aside from his two major inventions, Morgan also founded a line of hair-care products and started a newspaper for African Americans. Morgan was charitable with his wealth and donated money to many black colleges.

10.   Morgan died on July 27, 1963. He was responsible for some of the most helpful inventions in history. Though many people may not recognize his name, plenty of people are grateful for the contributions he made to American life.

Garrett Morgan Time Line

1877	born on March 4
1895	moved to Cleveland; worked in a repair shop
1907	opened repair shop
1909	opened tailor shop
1916	used gas mask to rescue 32 people trapped in a tunnel
1920	started the *Cleveland Call*, a newspaper
1963	died on July 27

COMMON CORE
STATE STANDARDS
W.6.1–
W.6.10

Name_____ Date_____

 Argument Prompt

Which of Garrett Morgan's inventions do you think was the most helpful? Support your opinion with details from the text.

 Informative/Explanatory Prompt

The author says "Morgan had a very mechanical mind." How does the author support this conclusion? Use details and quotations from the text to support your explanation.

 Narrative Prompt

Write a journal entry Garrett Morgan may have recorded after he used his hood to rescue workers trapped in a tunnel under Lake Erie.

COMMON CORE
STATE STANDARDS
**W.6.1–
W.6.10**

Name_____ Date_____

Read the passage below.

How to Make a Clay Volcano

1. A volcano is a mountain from which molten rock, or magma, erupts. There are thousands of volcanoes throughout the world. When a volcano erupts, extremely hot lava flows from it.

2. A volcanic eruption can be a spectacular sight, but it can cause great damage to the area around the volcano. It's possible to safely make a clay volcano that actually erupts!

3. Several items are needed to make a clay volcano. Gather the following materials:

   - empty water bottle
   - modeling clay
   - a baking pan
   - warm water
   - liquid dish detergent
   - baking soda
   - vinegar

4. The first step is to create the cone, or body, of the volcano out of clay. Place the water bottle on a flat surface. Then, form the modeling clay around the bottle, making a wide base to resemble a mountain. Be sure to keep the mouth of the bottle open because you will pour other ingredients into the volcano. Also be certain that the clay doesn't get inside the bottle.

5. Once the clay volcano is fully formed, place it in the middle of the baking pan. The eruption will cause "lava" to spew from the top of the volcano, so the baking pan will contain the "lava."

(continued)

Name_____ Date_____

(continued)

6.   Fill the bottle inside the volcano about halfway with warm water. Then, add a few drops of liquid dish detergent. Next, pour about two tablespoons of baking soda into the volcano.

7.   The final step will cause the volcano to erupt. Carefully pour about a quarter cup of vinegar into the volcano, and quickly back away from it.

8.   The baking soda and vinegar will undergo a chemical reaction, and the dish detergent will trap bubbles of gas. The mixture will fizz and spew from the mouth of the volcano, much like lava erupting from a real volcano.

9.   Add more baking soda and vinegar to see the volcano erupt again and again!

Name_____ Date_____

COMMON CORE
STATE STANDARDS
W.6.1–
W.6.10

Argument Prompt

Do you think a clay volcano is a good project for science class? Why or why not? Use details from the text to support your opinion.

Informative/Explanatory Prompt

Summarize the steps you would take to make a clay volcano. Use specific details from "How to Make a Clay Volcano."

Narrative Prompt

Write a story about two students who make a clay volcano that does not erupt. Have the students discuss what they may have done wrong. Use specific details from "How to Make a Clay Volcano."

Common Core
State Standards

W.6.1–
W.6.10

Name_____ Date_____

Read the passage below.

Education in Athens and Sparta

1.   Ancient Greece was made up of a network of city-states. Of these city-states, Athens and Sparta were the most powerful and influential. Other than this, however, the people of Athens and Sparta had little in common. This was especially true when it came to their educational systems.

2.   The people of Athens and Sparta both valued education but for different reasons. People in Athens thought education was a way to make young individuals intelligent. They considered education to be equally important in times of war and peace.

3.   The Spartans, on the other hand, turned to education as a way to create highly skilled soldiers for their military. The educational systems that developed in each city-state reflected the values of its people.

4.   Boys in Athens began their education at an early age. Girls did not receive a formal education. Some learned what they could at home, but many never learned more than how to perform household chores.

5.   Boys were taught at home until they were about seven years old. At this time, they went to primary schools to begin their formal education. Their education consisted of both physical and academic studies. They exercised, learned to play games, and, as they grew older, mastered fighting and military skills. Boys were also required to study literature, mathematics, and the arts.

(continued)

Common Core Writing to Texts Grade 6 • ©2014 Newmark Learning, LLC

Name_____ Date_____

COMMON CORE
STATE STANDARDS
W.6.1–
W.6.10

(continued)

6. When an Athenian boy reached the age of fourteen, he either became an apprentice or, if his family had enough money, continued his education.

7. At eighteen, regardless of his level of education, he was expected to attend military school for two years. After that, he might continue his education at an academy.

8. Spartan boys also started their formal education at age seven. However, they attended military school, which was very strict. They had to endure extremely harsh conditions and were expected to become hardened soldiers.

9. Their training included wrestling, boxing, and swimming. They continued to train in this manner until they were eighteen. At this time, they were turned loose and expected to steal their food as a way of proving their skills.

10. When they turned twenty, boys took difficult tests to determine whether they were ready for military service. If they passed, they entered the military and remained in service until they turned sixty.

11. Spartan girls were educated as well. Like boys, they started school at age seven and took part in many physical activities. The purpose of their education was different, however. Girls were trained for motherhood, as the Spartans believed that strong mothers produced strong soldiers.

Did you know?

• Books were rare in Athens. Boys mostly memorized lessons in school.

• Boys in Athens studied Homer, the Greek epic poet, and learned to play a musical instrument called the lyre.

• In Sparta, both boys and girls were expected to have a perfect body.

• Boys and girls in Sparta lived in their schools— they trained, studied, and slept there.

• While the Spartans believed learning to read and write was important, they thought learning to fight was much more important.

COMMON CORE
STATE STANDARDS

W.6.1–
W.6.10

Name_____ Date_____

Argument Prompt

Imagine that you are a child in ancient Greece. Would you rather live in Athens or Sparta? Support your opinion with reasons from the text.

Informative/Explanatory Prompt

Compare and contrast how girls were educated in Athens and Sparta. Use details from the text to support your explanation.

Narrative Prompt

Write a story from the point of view of a boy or girl growing up in Sparta. Using the first-person point of view, tell what your life is like.

Common Core Writing to Texts Grade 6 • ©2014 Newmark Learning, LLC

Name_____ Date_____

COMMON CORE
STATE STANDARDS
W.6.1–
W.6.10

Read the passage below.

Catching a Dinosaur

1.   I remember it like it was yesterday—the day I helped catch what was practically a living dinosaur!

2.   In December 1938, I was living in South Africa and working aboard a fishing ship, the Nerine. It was my job to operate the large trawling net that caught fish for us to sell at local markets. After being on this job for several months, I could drop and raise the net quickly and without tangles.

3.   On one particular voyage, we were sailing along the eastern coast of South Africa, approaching the mouth of the Chalumna River. We knew that this area was a hot spot for fish, and we dropped our net eagerly.

4.   As the ship dragged the net, crew members enjoyed the tropical breeze and talked about their great adventures. I remember feeling regretful that nothing truly remarkable had ever happened to me. I had no idea this day would change that fact.

5.   Our captain, Hendrick Goosen, came to see us. He smiled warmly and said he had a feeling we made a good catch today and asked me to pull in the net so we could see for ourselves.

6.   I did just that. I was so used to the process I acted as if by clockwork. The heavy net slowly rose through the water and the crew gathered around. When the dripping net swung onto the deck, however, we saw something very unusual. Among the regular fish we expected to see was a monstrous five-foot-long blue animal!

7.   "What a bizarre catch," said Captain Goosen. None of us had ever seen such a thing.

(continued)

COMMON CORE
STATE STANDARDS

W.6.1–
W.6.10

Name_____ Date_____

(continued)

8.   Some of the older sailors gathered around it. Some tried to compare it to other fish, but James Thompson remarked, "It looks like a dinosaur to me!" We laughed at the time, but once the laughter ended, we could not think of any better explanation.

9.   Once we came ashore, Captain Goosen hurried to find a telephone. We asked if he was calling the fish market, but he said, "No, I'm calling the museum!"

10.   Later that day, Marjorie Courtenay-Latimer, curator of the East London Museum and a fan of unusual fish, arrived. She was stunned to see our catch and immediately hired a taxi to bring it back to her laboratory. The taxi driver certainly was surprised!

11.   A few days later we learned that some of the top scientists in the world were discussing our find. They could not locate a single picture of this fish in any book; the closest matches were on prehistoric fossils.

12.   The scientists' explanation? The animal we caught that day was a coelacanth (SEE-luh-kanth), a fish believed to be dead millions of years ago! Coelacanths roamed the seas more than 300 million years ago, long before the dinosaurs!

13.   Since that time, I've known I was part of a truly remarkable event.

Name_____ Date_____

COMMON CORE
STATE STANDARDS
W.6.1–
W.6.10

Argument Prompt

Do you think it would be interesting to work on a fishing boat in South Africa? Support your opinion with facts from the text.

Informative/Explanatory Prompt

Why was the coelacanth different from other fish? Support your explanation with facts and quotations from the text.

Narrative Prompt

Write a journal that Marjorie Courtenay-Latimer may have recorded after taking the fish back to her laboratory.

COMMON CORE
STATE STANDARDS
W.6.1–
W.6.10

Name_____ Date_____

Read the passages.

The Hare with Many Friends
(an adaptation of Aesop's fable)

1. One evening, Hare entertained his many friends late into the night with an elegant dinner, delicious dessert, and pleasant music. Hare overslept and spent the next morning cleaning up from the party before sitting down to a light lunch of celery sticks and alfalfa sprouts.

2. As he nibbled, he recalled the conversations he'd enjoyed with his many guests the previous evening. *I have more friends than I can count*, he thought. *I am fortunate to have so many wonderful friends who adore me as much as I adore them.*

3. That afternoon, Hare decided to pay a visit to his friend Horse. His quiet stroll to the farm was interrupted suddenly by the distant barking of hounds. Alarmed, Hare scurried under the fence and raced across the field, where he discovered Horse relaxing beside a tree.

4. "Please help me, Horse!" cried Hare. "I can hear the hounds approaching! Please carry me away on your back before they arrive and capture me!"

5. Horse shook her head. "I have an extremely busy schedule today," she said. "The farmer and I have a tremendous amount of work to complete, but I'm positive your other friends will aid you." Horse turned and walked away, flicking her tail.

6. "Goodness!" cried Hare, scampering toward the barn where he found Goat standing in the open doorway. "Goat, please help me," begged Hare excitedly. "The hounds will chase me and catch me if you don't carry me away on your back!"

7. Goat was shocked by the request. "Surely you are a heavy burden for my slender back," he replied dismissively. "I'm afraid you must seek assistance elsewhere." Goat then trotted away.

8. Hare found Calf resting in the barn and again requested aid. "Please help me!" he begged, anxious to escape. "Neither Horse nor Goat would rescue me from the hounds!"

(continued)

Common Core Writing to Texts Grade 6 • ©2014 Newmark Learning, LLC

Name_____ Date_____

COMMON CORE
STATE STANDARDS
W.6.1–
W.6.10

(continued)

9.   Calf declined, saying, "If my elders aren't able to assist, then I should follow their example." He settled down, closed his eyes, and slumbered peacefully.

10.   By now, the hounds were drawing very near and Hare became frantic. He raced outside, wriggled under a fence, galloped across a meadow, and entered the forest. Hare's heart was pounding and he was terrified, but he continued to run.

11.   In time, the hounds' barking grew faint and Hare eventually hid in a briar patch, panting and exhausted. He decided to change his views regarding his friends; in the future, he would focus on the quality of his relationships rather than the quantity.

(continue to next passage)

COMMON CORE
STATE STANDARDS
W.6.1–
W.6.10

Name_____ Date_____

(continued)

The Goat Herder and the Wild Goats
(an adaptation of Aesop's fable)

1. One day, a young goat herder named Billy noticed that several wild goats had wandered into the meadow where his herd nibbled vegetation. Billy considered himself a clever fellow, and while he herded his goats together, he remained cautious around the wild animals.

2. *I shall allow the wild goats to remain in the midst of my goats*, Billy thought. *Then I will increase the size of my herd when I return to the farm.* He made himself agreeable to the wild goats, reassuring them of his gentleness by moving quietly among the herd.

3. Late in the afternoon, Billy rounded up his goats, herded them back to the farm, and confined them in the barn. He separated the wild goats into a vacant stall, where they regarded Billy with distrust. "We are not livestock," sniffed a wild goat to his companions later that night, but they were unable to escape, so they slumbered in the darkness.

4. A storm arrived during the night. The temperature dropped and snow fell all night and all day, blanketing the farm and fields. When Billy awoke and discovered the harsh weather outside, he hastened to the barn to care for his animals. Because he wanted the wild goats to stay with him, Billy was extremely generous in providing plentiful portions of good grain for them to eat. The goat herder distributed small rations to his animals, however, and the tame goats compared their stingy portion with the luxury served to the newcomers. "Billy betrays us by giving abundant grain to the strangers," complained the eldest goat in discussion with the rest of the herd.

5. For two days Billy remained in his snug dwelling, emerging only to care for his livestock. He took considerable care with the wild goats, always distributing superior food in abundant quantities to them, but remained stingy with his own goats. Finally, on the third day, the sun began to melt the snow. Billy trudged through the slush and freed the goats. His herd eagerly trotted outside to find vegetation, but the wild goats raced toward the woods.

6. "Wait!" Billy called, annoyed that the newcomers were running away. "I have treated you well and kept you in luxury. Why won't you stay?"

7. The wild goats paused warily. "Yesterday you treated us well while your own herd starved," called a wild goat. "We would expect such poor treatment from you in the future if other goats arrived in your barn." The wild goats leaped into the forest and never returned to Billy's farm.

     Common Core Writing to Texts Grade 6 • ©2014 Newmark Learning, LLC

Name_____ Date_____

COMMON CORE
STATE STANDARDS
W.6.1–
W.6.10

 Argument Prompt

Who do you think learns a more important lesson, Hare or Billy?
Support your opinion with facts from both texts.

 Informative/Explanatory Prompt

Compare and contrast Hare's friends in "The Hare with Many
Friends" and the wild goats in "The Goat Herder and the Wild
Goats." Explain how they are alike and different using details from
both texts.

 Narrative Prompt

Write a story in which Billy of "The Goat Herder and the Wild Goats"
and Hare of "The Hare with Many Friends" become friends. Keep in
mind the lessons they have both learned about friendship.

Name_____ Date_____

Read the passages.

Georgia Summer

Chapter 1

1. The bright pink envelope sat on the kitchen counter with the rest of the day's mail, and a wave of excitement washed over Shannon. Was that a much-desired invitation to Kelly Weatherly's twelfth birthday party? After checking the name on the front of the envelope, Shannon tore it open and removed the contents. A shower of colorful confetti dowsed her feet as she pulled out a glossy invitation. "Come celebrate with us!" the invitation shouted in bold, brightly colored letters surrounded by images of balloons and streamers. Shannon slowly turned the invitation over and read the details:

You're invited to a pool party!

To honor
Kelly Weatherly's
12th Birthday
please join us for a
POOL PARTY
Saturday, June 3
2 P.M. to 5 P.M.
RSVP by May 27

2. The bottom of the invitation included a phone number and directions to Kelly Weatherly's house. Shannon sighed and slumped onto a stool. She knew she should be thrilled. After all, Kelly, the most popular girl in Shannon's class, had just invited her, the new girl in school, to THE social event of the summer. Nonetheless, Shannon couldn't help but feel glum, and she started to think about the town in northern Maine where she had grown up.

(continued)

Name_____ Date_____

(continued)

3.   In her old neighborhood, very few people had pools in their backyards. The summers were usually pleasant—sunny and warm rather than beastly hot and humid. On the hottest days, Shannon and her friends used to dash through the sprinkler or have water balloon fights. They somehow managed to keep cool without ever submerging themselves into three to ten feet of chlorinated water.

4.   A couple months ago, however, Shannon's dad, a history professor, was offered a job at a university in Georgia, and her family left northern Maine. In Shannon's new neighborhood, just about everyone owned a swimming pool of some sort and with good reason. The temperatures in January often climbed into the mid-seventies and by April and May reached the mid-eighties. Shannon still hadn't adjusted to Georgia's blazing sun and high humidity.

5.   On a few particularly hot days, some of her new friends had invited her to beat the heat in their swimming pools, but Shannon had politely declined. She had lied and said she had a doctor appointment, a dentist appointment, a haircut; her most recent excuse had been a music lesson. *Well*, thought Shannon as she gathered her books to retreat to her bedroom, *I'll just have to think of something really good this time*.

6.   As Shannon tossed her books on her bed, the phone rang. Shannon answered and immediately recognized her friend Amanda's excited squeal.

7.   "No excuses—you're going to Kelly's party with me!" Amanda exclaimed.

8.   "I—I—I can't make it that day," said Shannon, tripping over her words. "I have a, um, thing to, uh, do."

9.   Shannon kicked herself for blurting out the weakest excuse in history.

10.   "Oh no," said Amanda, "you're not pulling that. I'm your friend, and it's time to confess. You can't swim, can you?"

(continue to next passage)

COMMON CORE
STATE STANDARDS
W.6.1–
W.6.10

Name_____ Date_____

(continued)

Chapter 2

1.   Shannon sat in silence on the edge of her bed. Finally, she replied to Amanda's accusation. "No, I can't swim."

2.   "Shannon, I am your best friend. Why didn't you tell me sooner?" asked Amanda.

3.   "I was embarrassed," explained Shannon. "Everyone here seems to have learned to swim when they were infants, and I thought that if I revealed that I couldn't swim that I wouldn't fit in."

4.   "Oh, Shannon, that's a silly reason to miss out on a really fun activity," said Amanda. "Listen, you have two full weeks before you have to RSVP for the party, and it just so happens that my mom is the swim instructor at the YMCA. You're coming to my house tomorrow for your first swim lesson, and I promise you, she'll have you swimming like a guppy in no time."

5.   Shannon tried to object, but Amanda pretended not to hear her and hung up.

6.   That night, Shannon reluctantly dug through her clothes to the back of her closet, where she found her old swimsuit crumpled in a ball on the floor. She tossed it into a bag with a beach towel, a pair of flip-flops, and a bottle of water-resistant sunscreen. She was about to crawl into bed when a knock sounded on her door and her mother appeared.

7.   "Hey, sweetie, are you okay?" asked Mom. "You seemed kind of quiet at dinner tonight, and I thought for sure you'd be excited about the invitation to Kelly's party."

8.   "You must not have looked too closely at the invitation," said Shannon. "It's a pool party, and I can't swim."

9.   "Well, you can still have fun at the party without swimming, can't you?" Mom asked.

10.   "Probably, but I didn't tell you the worst part. Now Amanda knows and she wants me to go to her house tomorrow to get swim lessons from her mother! I'm so embarrassed," said Shannon, burying her head in her pillow.

11.   Mom stroked Shannon's hair. "I know you don't want to hear this," she said, "but this isn't the end of the world, Shannon. It'll be good for you to learn."

12.   Shannon's mother left the room, turning the light out behind her, and Shannon rolled over and stared at the ceiling. When she finally drifted off to sleep, she dreamed of bottomless pits of water and sky-high waves.

COMMON CORE
STATE STANDARDS
W.6.1–
W.6.10

Name_____ Date_____

Argument Prompt

Do you think Shannon will enjoy swimming after her lessons? Why or why not? Support your opinion with details from both chapters of the novel.

Informative/Explanatory Prompt

Shannon moved to Georgia from Maine. Explain how this is significant to the plot of the novel. Use details from both chapters to support your explanation.

Narrative Prompt

Write a third chapter of the book in which Shannon learns to swim. Use details from Chapters 1 and 2 to make a smooth transition into Chapter 3.

COMMON CORE
STATE STANDARDS
W.6.1–
W.6.10

Name_____ Date_____

Read the passages.

Dalia's Dilemma

1. "You're going to Brooke's sleepover, right?" Lena asked her best friend, Dalia.

2. "I wouldn't miss it for anything," Dalia responded.

3. Brooke was having a sleepover Saturday night for all her friends, and Dalia and Lena were invited. Brooke's parents were the coolest parents ever, always providing the best food and games whenever the group of friends got together. At the last sleepover Brooke hosted, the girls stayed up late, chatting and picking on delicious snacks.

4. After school the next day, Dalia was busy working on a science project when her mom interrupted her.

5. "Don't forget about helping Grandma this weekend," Mom said.

6. Dalia looked up from her work and asked, "That's during the day on Saturday, right? Because Brooke's sleepover is that night."

7. "No, it's not during the day," Mom said. "Remember I told you? Grandma is volunteering all day at the veterans' center, and then needs help baking cookies Saturday night."

8. Grandma had asked Dalia to help bake an assortment of cookies on Saturday night that were needed for a Sunday afternoon function at the veterans' center.

9. Grandma was very busy lately, spending much of her time volunteering at the veterans' center, and the only free time she had for baking was Saturday night. When Grandma had asked Dalia to help bake, Dalia had promised to help, forgetting that it would conflict with Brooke's sleepover. Now she wished she had told Grandma that she was busy and couldn't help.

10. On Saturday morning, Dalia woke up in a bad mood. Although she knew it was selfish, she didn't want to have to sacrifice Brooke's sleepover to help Grandma that night. She contemplated going to the sleepover instead of helping Grandma.

(continued)

Common Core Writing to Texts Grade 6 • ©2014 Newmark Learning, LLC

Name_____ Date_____

COMMON CORE
STATE STANDARDS
W.6.1–
W.6.10

(continued)

11. Dalia was tormented over her dilemma all afternoon. On one hand, she wanted to have fun that night with Lena and her other friends, but on the other hand, she didn't want to let Grandma down.

12. She tried to think about the situation with a clear head. If she missed the sleepover, she would be out of the loop with her friends. Then again, if she went to the sleepover, Grandma wouldn't be able to get all of her baking done, and the people at the veterans' center would be disappointed.

13. Ultimately, Dalia decided to help Grandma. As it turned out, there was one thing Dalia would miss the sleepover for—doing the right thing.

(continue to next passage)

COMMON CORE
STATE STANDARDS
W.6.1–
W.6.10

Name_____ Date_____

(continued)

Eric's Essay

1. Eric let out a sigh and threw his arms up in the air. "This essay is impossible!" he exclaimed, slamming his hand on the kitchen table. His mom came over to see what the commotion was all about.

2. "Mr. Wallace is such a hard teacher," Eric whined to Mom. "If it's alright, I'm going over to Brianna's to see if she can help me with this essay. She had Mr. Wallace last year."

3. Mom gave her consent, and Eric went to visit Brianna, who lived just a few blocks away. Although Brianna was a year older than Eric, the two friends developed a strong bond over the years, often helping one another whenever a problem arose for one of them.

4. Once he arrived at Brianna's house, Eric greeted her parents and went into the kitchen where Brianna was doing her homework. He explained that he was having difficulty with the essay and asked Brianna if she remembered writing it last year.

5. Nodding her head, Brianna told Eric she remembered the essay, and then said, "You know what I did? I used Russ Turner's essay from the year before. I just changed a few sentences here and there, and then turned it in."

6. A startled look came across Eric's face. In all the years he had known Brianna, he never would have guessed that she was brazen enough to cheat like that.

7. Brianna began rummaging through a bunch of papers on her desk, removed one of them, and handed it to Eric. "Here's my essay," she said. "Feel free to use it, but just make sure you change it around a little bit."

8. Reluctantly, Eric took the paper, but he didn't know what to say. He managed a faint "Thanks," folded the paper in half, and stuffed it in his pocket.

9. Back home, Eric sat on his bed, staring blankly at the paper Brianna had given him. It would be so easy to just copy Brianna's essay, revise a few sentences, and then be done with it. But at the same time, he knew he would feel guilty afterward for cheating. He simply didn't know what to do.

10. A few days later, Eric was sitting in class when Mr. Wallace asked everyone to pass forward their essays. Eric nervously handed in his essay, unsure of himself. But one thing he was sure of was that he had turned in an essay that was all his own.

Name_____ Date_____

COMMON CORE
STATE STANDARDS
**W.6.1–
W.6.10**

Argument Prompt

What is one theme that can be applied to both stories? Support your opinion with facts and details from both "Dalia's Dilemma" and "Eric's Essay."

Informative/Explanatory Prompt

Explain how Dalia and Eric are alike. Support your explanation with details from both texts.

Narrative Prompt

Imagine that Dalia and Eric are at a farmer's market and one of the farmers has a stand but is not there. The farmer has left a note by a basket that reads, "Please leave money for fruit and vegetables here." Some kids they don't know take food without paying. Write a story in which Dalia and Eric meet and discuss the kids' behavior and why it was wrong. Include dialogue in your story.

Name_____ Date_____

Read the passages.

The Art of Patience

1.   Henka, Rini, and Dagmar shuffled through stacks of colorful papers. Dagmar quickly chose a blue-and-white striped sheet, while Henka found orange dotted paper and Rini chose a solid green sheet. The ten-year-old chums studied the pages of the book before them on the table.

2.   "I wonder how your paper dog will look with stripes," said Rini, glancing at Dagmar's paper.

3.   "Blue-striped dogs are the best," Dagmar replied, grinning, as he began folding the paper carefully. As he followed the directions in the origami book, his paper gradually began to resemble an animal. Soon it had a head, a tail, and legs, and with another fold Dagmar gave it a nose.

4.   "Oh, your dog looks terrific," said Henka, working on her spotted paper dog's head. She was nearly finished, though Rini was a few steps behind her in the paper-folding project. Henka completed her dog's nose, too, and stood it on the table beside the striped dog. A minute later, when Rini's green dog joined the paper-dog pack, Dagmar and Henka were already sorting through the stack of papers.

5.   "What shall we make next?" Rini asked, turning the pages of the book. She considered the instructions for a bird project. "Ooh, this looks like a parrot!" Rini said, showing it to her friends.

6.   "The parrot looks much more difficult than the dog," Henka said anxiously, studying the book.

7.   "The point of trying something new is to challenge ourselves," Dagmar reminded her. He flourished several sheets of colorful paper. "Would anyone like to make a pansy parrot?"

8.   Rini laughed and reached for the paper. "Absolutely, pansies make the best parrots!" She briefly studied the first set of instructions and began folding her paper. Henka hesitated before making a selection and copying Rini's folds.

9.   "It was very thoughtful of your mother to buy the book," Rini said to Dagmar.

(continued)

Name_____ Date_____

COMMON CORE
STATE STANDARDS
W.6.1–
W.6.10

(continued)

10. "She was on a business trip last week," Dagmar explained. "After her meetings, she was bored, so she went to a museum. She saw an amazing exhibit of Japanese art that included some modern folded paper art and later she noticed the book in the museum shop."

11. Dagmar paused while he concentrated on folding his paper. "It really was thoughtful of her," he continued, "so I'm going to glue magnets to my parrot and puppy so she can hang them on her memo board at the office."

12. Rini and Henka agreed that it was a good idea, and for several minutes the friends focused silently on their projects. Dagmar and Rini completed their parrots first and offered suggestions as Henka worked on the tricky folds.

13. "Is that right?" Henka asked, smoothing out the parrot's tail as her friends nodded.

14. "See, we just had to concentrate," said Rini, grinning. "Slow but steady wins the race."

(continue to next passage)

Name_____ Date_____

(continued)

Henka's Race

1.   Henka jogged in place and looked across the track field. She quickly glanced at her competition. As she retied the laces on her sneakers, she realized the opposite side seemed impossibly distant. As Henka stood, Dagmar raised his arm and looked at his watch. "On your mark, get set, go!" he yelled. Henka sped away, pumping her arms and legs and feeling her hair streaming behind her. By the time she approached the finish line, however, she was exhausted.

2.   "I timed some other girls while I waited for you this afternoon," Dagmar said as they approached. "Unfortunately, they ran two hundred meters much more swiftly."

3.   Henka looked miserable, but Rini offered encouragement and draped her arm across her friend's shoulders. "The race is a month away. You have plenty of time to increase your speed," she said.

4.   Dagmar noticed Henka was still gasping. "You should also increase your endurance," he said. "My coach always reminds us to stay active during the off-season with regular exercise. My little brother likes to go to the park, so we ride our bikes there together."

5.   Rini reminded her friends that Henka's father had agreed to help his daughter train, but Henka feared she had waited too long to ask him for help. First, she'd delayed training until the weather improved, then she'd been distracted by plans for the upcoming spring festival, and now she had only a few weeks to prepare. Henka shrugged. "He's so busy that he doesn't run as often as he'd like, and time is running out," she said.

6.   "Slow but steady wins the race, Henka," said Dagmar, reminding her of Rini's favorite phrase.

7.   "In four weeks, you will be swift and steady," Rini said, grinning. "My mom is a jogger, so if your dad works late, ask him if you can run with us."

8.   For the next four weeks, Rini made sure that Henka had jogging partners when her father was busy. Dagmar invited Henka to cycle with him and his brother to the park, and Henka's endurance gradually improved. On race day, she saw Dagmar and Rini waiting with her parents beside the stands.

9.   "Henka, how are you feeling?" Dagmar asked her as she approached.

10.   "I'm ready to run, and I think I can win," Henka announced excitedly.

11.   Rini grinned at her friend. "Your endurance and speed have improved. All you have to do is finish the race, Henka, because you're already a winner."

Name_____ Date_____

COMMON CORE
STATE STANDARDS
W.6.1–
W.6.10

Argument Prompt

Which character do you think is more helpful, Rini or Dagmar? Use facts and quotations from both stories to support your opinion.

Informative/Explanatory Prompt

In both "The Art of Patience" and "Henka's Race," the characters say "Slow but steady wins the race." Explain why this statement is significant to the plot of each story.

Narrative Prompt

Write a sequel to "Henka's Race" in which Henka competes in the race while Rini and Dagmar watch. Use details from both stories to tell what the characters say and do.

COMMON CORE
STATE STANDARDS
W.6.1–
W.6.10

Name_____ Date_____

Read the passages.

Stage Lights

1. The barren stage beckons as I approach,
2. A beggar seeking crumbs of approval and applause.
3. Will I be loved or betrayed by the faces in the front row?
4. Will the curtain fall on stonefaced silence,
5. Crushing my career, my soul, my dreams?

6. (Girl meets boy in act one.
7. Gazing and engaging, fear and doubt prevail.
8. Troubles take their toll but finally,
9. By final scene we find the truth:
10. Their love has conquered all.)

11. Following custom the cast assembles,
12. Grasping hands, bowing deeply, seeking support,
13. Absorbing the adoration of the audience,
14. Carefully collecting it like bouquets—flowers to feed the spirit.
15. The light glows, warming me. I bloom. I am loved.

(continue to next passage)

COMMON CORE
STATE STANDARDS
W.6.1–
W.6.10

Name_____ Date_____

(continued)

Stage Fright

1.   Twelve-year-old Jade rummaged through her book bag, dug out a pencil, and swiftly signed her name on the audition list. As she turned to hurry to class, she nearly knocked over her friend Noel.

2.   "Oh, sorry!" Jade apologized, stumbling back against the notice board.

3.   "It's okay," said Noel, reading the audition notice over her shoulder. "You're going to audition for the school play? You don't even like giving reports in class. How are you going to perform in front of an auditorium filled with people?"

4.   Jade groaned, disappointed that her friend would remind her of her fears. "I don't want to think about the audience," she said. "I really like this play and I've always wanted to perform, so I'm just going to try to get a part."

5.   Noel knew how much Jade feared being on stage and admired her courage. "Okay, I'm in," she said, taking Jade's pencil and adding her name to the roster. "I've never heard of the play and I've never wanted to perform, but I'll audition with you and see what happens."

6.   Jade felt relieved because if Noel was auditioning, too, they could support one another. "History first and theater later," Jade said as the bell rang.

7.   At the afternoon audition, Jade dealt with her nervousness by trying several relaxation exercises. She closed her eyes, breathed slowly, and imagined she was in a quiet place. Noel sat beside her, studying the "Downtown Depot" script while a constant stream of students climbed on stage, read the lines, and returned to the audience.

(continued)

COMMON CORE
STATE STANDARDS

W.6.1–
W.6.10

Name_____ Date_____

(continued)

8.   Finally, the English teacher, Ms. Govern, called Jade, Noel, and several others to line up for their auditions. Jade suddenly felt nervous and dawdled, so she was at the end of the column. Noel was still choosing a character when she was called, so she simply read the first lines of the script.

9.   Ms. Govern smiled, and Jade tried not to laugh because Noel was taking the role of a male character. Noel grinned when she discovered her mistake, began again, and bowed cheerfully when everyone applauded.

10.   Jade breathed deeply as she walked to the center of the stage. She had chosen her role long ago and said her lines without reading the script. As Jade and Noel left, the teacher said that she would post the results in the morning.

11.   Noel was waiting for Jade the next day, and together they inched through the crowd around the notice board to read the cast names.

12.   "Congratulations!" Jade said as she realized Noel had won a part in "Downtown Depot."

13.   "The same to you," Noel replied, grinning as Jade studied the list and discovered she had earned a starring role.

14.   "This is going to be amazing!" Jade exclaimed, suddenly excited about opening night and unconcerned about the audience. "Our characters are in numerous scenes, so we'll be at rehearsal together most of the time."

Name_____ Date_____

COMMON CORE
STATE STANDARDS
W.6.1–
W.6.10

Argument Prompt

Do you think the poem "Stage Lights" or the story "Stage Fright" better illustrates what it is like to perform on stage? Support your opinion with details from both the poem and the story.

Informative/Explanatory Prompt

Compare and contrast the speaker of the poem and Jade. Use facts and quotations from both "Stage Lights" and "Stage Fright" to explain how they are alike and different.

Narrative Prompt

Write a story in which Jade meets the speaker of the poem "Stage Lights." Give the speaker of the poem a name. Have Jade and the speaker discuss what it is like to be in a play. Include dialogue in your story.

COMMON CORE
STATE STANDARDS
W.6.1–
W.6.10

Name_____ Date_____

Read the passages.

The Daily News

SUNDAY, JANUARY 3, 1892

Ellis Island Becomes a Gateway to America

1. January 2, 1892 – The new federal immigration station at Ellis Island began processing new arrivals in the United States for the first time today. With its historic opening, Ellis Island becomes one of the main points of entry for immigrants looking to start a new life in America. It replaces the Castle Garden station that was previously operated by the state of New York.

2. Ellis Island, on which the new station was built, has a long local history. It was originally known to Native Americans who lived in the area as Kioshk Island. Over the years since European settlers arrived, it has been known by a number of other names, including Oyster, Bucking, and Anderson's Island. It was later named Ellis Island after Samuel Ellis, the private owner of the island in the 1770s.

3. During the Revolutionary War, it became clear that New York Harbor was dangerously open to attacks from invading naval ships. Sensing the need to prepare for what eventually became the War of 1812, the federal government purchased Ellis Island in 1808 and built a fort there. Fort Gibson, as it was called, was part of the harbor defense system that protected New York City for many years.

4. In 1855, the Castle Garden immigration center was opened. At the time,

(continued)

Common Core Writing to Texts Grade 6 • ©2014 Newmark Learning, LLC

Name_____ Date_____

Common Core
State Standards
W.6.1–
W.6.10

(continued)

The Daily News

COPY PRICE 20 CENTS

each state was responsible for its own immigration system. Between 1855 and 1890, Castle Garden processed about eight million immigrants. In its final years, however, the station was faced with a growing number of problems. Most importantly, the changing political situation in Europe forced a much larger number of immigrants than expected to flee to America.

5. Castle Garden eventually proved to be too small to handle the scores of immigrants attempting to enter the country. The station also struggled with poor leadership and bad practices.

6. When the federal government took control of the immigration system in 1890, the decision was made to close Castle Garden in favor of building a new immigration center on Ellis Island. Construction of the new station took about two years to complete. While it was being built, new immigrants were processed at the Barge Office at the Battery.

7. The new Ellis Island processing center was officially opened on January 1. It began operations the next day. Three Irish children, fifteen-year-old Annie Moore and her two brothers, became the first immigrants to pass through the new station. They made the difficult journey from Ireland to meet their parents, who were already living in New York City. In its first full day of operation, the Ellis Island station processed about 700 immigrants. It is expected that thousands and thousands more will pass through in the coming years.

(continue to next passage)

COMMON CORE
STATE STANDARDS
W.6.1–
W.6.10

Name_____ Date_____

(continued)

Ellis Island: Journey to America

1. After many months of waiting and dreaming, it was finally time to go to America. Almost a year ago my parents told me, my brother James, and my sister Margret that we would be leaving our home in Ireland to move to America as soon as we saved enough money.

2. Our journey began with a long trip to Cobh, where we would board the great ship that would take us to America. We packed what little we could take with us onto an old wagon and prepared to leave. As we pulled away and watched our old house disappear into the distance, James, the youngest, began to cry. He was really sad to leave, but Mother comforted him and assured him that he would be happy in America.

3. When we arrived in Cobh, there was a long line of people waiting to board the ship. We climbed aboard and headed to the lowest part of the ship, where all the people who could only afford the cheapest tickets stayed. It was so crowded that there was barely any room to move. The trip across the sea seemed to take forever and with so many people onboard, the ship grew smelly and hot. Being stuck on the ship for so long wasn't fun, but we made the best of it. Margret and I snuck up on deck to look at the water as often as we could. James stayed with our parents most of the time, still feeling homesick.

4. After the ship docked, we all had to make our way down a plank that led us onto land. We learned that we arrived at a place called Ellis Island. There was a huge swarm of people and countless workers shouting things in many different languages I had never heard before. We were quickly led up a long stairway and into a large room with many rows of people. James still seemed a little sad, but I could tell he was amazed by everything he saw.

5. In the big room, we were examined by doctors who needed to check to see if we were healthy. We then moved to a different part of the room where a man asked Father questions about where we came from, where we were going, and how much money we had. After this, the man told us we were ready to leave and showed us to another large staircase. When we reached the top of the stairs, we were finally able to see New York City—it was amazing! It looked like a forest of tall buildings! After a quick ferry ride, we arrived in the city. I looked over at James and saw that he had a big smile on his face. We had made it to America!

Name_____ Date_____

COMMON CORE
STATE STANDARDS
W.6.1–
W.6.10

Argument Prompt

Would you have liked to have been a new arrival at the immigration station at Ellis Island in the late 1800s? Why or why not? Support your opinion with details from both texts.

Informative/Explanatory Prompt

Explain what the immigration station at Ellis Island was like using facts and quotations from both "Ellis Island Becomes Gateway to America" and "Ellis Island: Journey to America."

Narrative Prompt

Write a story from the point of view of Annie Moore about what it was like to be processed at the immigration station at Ellis Island. Base your story on details from both texts.

COMMON CORE
STATE STANDARDS
W.6.1–
W.6.10

Name_____ Date_____

Read the passages.

Is Corn the Answer?

1.   Corn can be used as a source of energy. It is a renewable resource that is grown with solar energy, or the energy from the sun. Corn is processed to produce different energy products. For example, corn can be used to create a product called ethanol.

2.   This colorless liquid can be added to gasoline to reduce the amount of gasoline burned by vehicles. Shelled corn can be dried and formed into pellets. These pellets can be burned in special stoves to heat homes.

3.   Many groups oppose the use of corn as fuel. Agricultural specialists say that using corn for fuel does not really save Americans money. Instead, it causes the prices of all foods to go up. Corn is used in so many food products that when its price rises, the cost of using it in other food products rises, too. For example, a higher price for corn means the prices for cattle and chicken feed go up.

4.   In turn, consumers are then charged more for eggs, milk, and meat. Additionally, farmers who choose to plant corn for profit will plant fewer other crops. That means shortages— and price increases—can occur with those crops, too.

5.   Scientists say that another problem is that ethanol may reduce the efficiency of fuel. This means cars will burn more fuel on ethanol than they do when using just gas. Some experts also think that ethanol

(continued)

Name_____ Date_____

COMMON CORE
STATE STANDARDS
W.6.1–
W.6.10

(continued)

causes problems with car engines. Consumers will have to spend even more money repairing and replacing their vehicles.

6. Corn is a good heating agent. However, to use it as a heating source, consumers must purchase a special type of stove. These stoves are costly and require a great deal of upkeep. For example, the storage hopper must be filled with pellets on a daily basis. Then the stove itself needs to be maintained regularly so that it continues to operate as it should.

7. Finally, some researchers question why we should use food crops for fuel when so many people—especially in undeveloped countries of the world—are facing food shortages. These researchers believe it is unethical for food to be used for fuel when it should be used to feed the hungry.

(continue to next passage)

COMMON CORE
STATE STANDARDS
W.6.1–
W.6.10

Name_____ Date_____

(continued)

Heating with Corn

1. Despite recent advances in technology, the United States continues to face an energy crisis. This crisis is driven by the amount of fuel Americans burn each year to heat their homes. Historically, Americans have relied on fossil fuels for this type of fuel—especially coal, oil, and natural gas.

2. Burning fossil fuels is a problem for several reasons. Fossil fuels are nonrenewable resources. They take millions of years to form and are difficult to replace. Fossil fuels also cause us to rely too much on other countries. Although some of the fuel we burn for energy comes from the United States, much of it comes from other nations. This makes America too reliant on foreign suppliers. Finally, fossil fuels are known to create environmental problems. They release carbon dioxide, a greenhouse gas, into the air. This substance warms the surface of Earth and is considered one of the main causes of global warming.

3. A better choice is to burn shelled corn, or maize, for fuel. Corn is a renewable resource because more corn can be grown all the time. In fact, corn is very efficient as an energy source because it grows quickly. A corn crop can be brought from seed to harvest in only 180 days. Compare that to the millions of years it takes Earth to form coal!

4. Choosing a heating option like corn has some real benefits. It is much cheaper than traditional fuel sources, so consumers will pay less for the same heat. It also reduces our reliance on foreign suppliers. Because we can grow our own corn, we do not have to buy it from other countries. Also, the money America currently spends purchasing fuel from other nations will be kept in this country instead. This benefits everyone, but is especially important for farmers and agricultural workers.

5. Finally, unlike fossil fuels, corn burns "clean." It does not release carbon dioxide into the atmosphere. It does not contribute to environmental problems such as global warming. And, when corn is grown, it absorbs some of the extra carbon dioxide in the atmosphere. This means that growing more corn can help us to clean up problems already in the environment.

6. Some people oppose the use of corn for fuel because they think food supplies should be used only for food. Global hunger is a big problem. However, using corn for fuel does not impact this problem. Most issues with the food supply have to do with being able to store and deliver food to the hungry. These issues are not really related to the growth of food.

Name_____ Date_____

Argument Prompt

Do you think corn should be used as a source of heat? Support your opinion with facts and quotations from both texts.

Informative/Explanatory Prompt

Explain why some people think it is unethical to use corn for energy. Support your explanations with facts and quotations from "Is Corn the Answer?" and "Heating with Corn."

Narrative Prompt

Write a story about a researcher who gives a presentation to the student body of your school about using corn for energy instead of fossil fuels. Have students who are against using corn for energy ask the researcher questions. Give your characters names and include dialogue in your story.

COMMON CORE
STATE STANDARDS
W.6.1–
W.6.10

Name_____ Date_____

Read the passages.

State Bird Poster Contest

1. The annual State Bird Poster Contest seeks young artists to create posters exploring the variety and importance of birds. Each poster must include an original illustration of a state bird.

Introduction

2. Each state in the nation has chosen a bird species as a symbol. These birds are often selected because they represent some aspect of their state's nature. The purpose of the State Bird Poster Contest is to highlight the beauty and variety of state birds. It is also to draw attention to the problems these birds face and their importance on Earth.

3. Ongoing development and environmental issues frequently affect wildlife. Birds can be threatened by chemical use and the loss of the environment in which they live.

4. Scientists have discovered that birds benefit the environment in many ways. Some birds eat seeds and fruits. When they travel, they distribute seeds to a wide area. Fish eggs cling to the legs of wading birds and are redistributed in waterways. Other birds help plants by moving pollen from flower to flower. People benefit when birds eat insects. Many birds eat pests such as mosquitoes or caterpillars. These birds may eat many insects and also catch insects to feed to their chicks.

Prizes

5. The creators of the top ten state bird posters will be awarded $50 cash prizes. The grand prize is $100. One poster of each state bird will be published in a full-color book, which will be available online and in many museums. Winners' names will appear with all published versions of their posters.

(continued)

Name_____ Date_____

COMMON CORE
STATE STANDARDS
W.6.1–
W.6.10

(continued)

Rules

6.   The State Bird Poster Contest is open to all residents in the United States age eighteen and younger. One entry per person may be submitted.

7.   1. All art must be the resident's original creation.

8.   2. Posters must be vertical and measure twelve inches by eighteen inches.

9.   3. The bird must be the main focus of the poster. The name of the bird and the state must appear on the poster.

10.   4. A bird expert will judge each entry on technical correctness before advancing the poster for judging on artistic worth. Posters containing incorrect information will be removed from the competition.

11.   5. The outline of the state represented by the bird must appear on the poster. The outline must be at least two inches wide or deep.

12.   6. Artists must use pencils, markers, or paints on paper.

13.   7. The name and address of the artist must be written on the back of the entry.

14.   8. All entries become the property of the contest organizers. The judges' choice is final.

15.   9. Entries must be postmarked by December 31.

How to Enter

16.   Download the official entry form here. Entries must be mailed to the address on the entry form.

(continue to next passage)

COMMON CORE
STATE STANDARDS
W.6.1–
W.6.10

Name_____ Date_____

(continued)

State Bird Poster Contest Judge Profile: Roberto Hernandez

1.   Roberto Hernandez is an accomplished nature artist, educator, and activist. He has been awarded numerous honors and awards for his work. Hernandez organizes student art exhibitions around the world. His international efforts include working with young refugees on art therapy projects and exhibits. "Every young artist has a story," says Hernandez. "It's rewarding to me to help young people find ways to tell their stories and share their feelings through art."

2.   Hernandez grew up in a small town in Maryland, where as a student he enjoyed painting and working with clay. While attending college, he discovered mixed-media art, which is visual art in which the artist has used more than one medium. Hernandez began experimenting with paint, newspaper, and magazines to create mixed-media art with social issue messages. He earned success several years later when his mixed-media work *Exit Sign* was featured in a well-known gallery in New York.

3.   Soon the artist received his first monetary award, which allowed him to travel to South America. Hernandez visited remote villages, where he met with farmers to discuss the changes in their communities. He returned to these villages over the years, helping to build and support schools. Later, Hernandez helped several students attend college and art schools.

4.   Hernandez eventually bought a farm in Virginia, where he lives and operates an art school. Students from many countries study there and meet other artists who teach and take classes. Hernandez employs some of his former students as art teachers.

5.   Hernandez lives in Virginia with his wife, Sylvia, who operates a gallery featuring her husband's work and the creations of several of his students. The couple has two children, who often travel to refugee camps with their parents.

6.   Hernandez will be the final judge of the State Bird Poster Contest. Winners will be announced in February. The winning young artists will be flown to Washington, D.C. to attend a gallery opening and dinner party, where they will meet Hernandez and the other judges.

Name_____ Date_____

COMMON CORE
STATE STANDARDS
W.6.1–
W.6.10

Argument Prompt

Do you think Roberto Hernandez is qualified to be the final judge of the State Bird Poster Contest? Why or why not? Use facts from both texts to support your opinion.

Informative/Explanatory Prompt

Explain the judging process of the State Bird Poster Contest using details from both texts.

Narrative Prompt

Write a story from the point of view of a student who is one of the top ten winners of the State Bird Poster Contest. Explain which bird this student has drawn and how he or she feels about traveling to Washington, D.C. to meet Hernandez and the other judges.

COMMON CORE
STATE STANDARDS
W.6.1–
W.6.10

Name_____ Date_____

Read the passages.

Cnidarians

1.   Cnidarians (ny-DAIR-ee-unz) are a specific category of sea creatures with tentacles that can sting. *Cnidarian* literally means "stinging creature." Cnidarians use their stingers to disable their prey. Hydroids, jellyfish, anemones, and corals are cnidarians.

Description

2.   More than 9,000 species of cnidarians exist worldwide. Most are quite beautiful. Their body parts extend outward from their center, making them look like flowers. They are also symmetrical.

3.   Cnidarians have one of two body types: polypoid or medusoid. Polypoids have tentacles and a mouth that both face up. They are usually attached to a large colony of other stationary sea creatures.

4.   The stinging cells of a cnidarian are called cnidocytes. Cnidocytes contain a tiny, coil-like stinger called a nematocyst. When a cnidarian is trying to capture its prey, it triggers the nematocyst, which springs straight and pushes through the cnidocyte's wall to sting the prey. Some cnidarians's stingers produce a toxin that helps to further subdue their prey. All cnidarians have tentacles with stinging cells on the tips. They use their stingers to stun and capture their prey.

Behavior and Diet

5.   Some cnidarians are solitary creatures and must find their own food. Others exist within a large group connected by living tissue and share food. Most cnidarians feed on prey that they capture with their tentacles. Some cnidarians also feed on food particles and chemicals in water.

(continued)

 Common Core Writing to Texts Grade 6 • ©2014 Newmark Learning, LLC

Name_____ Date_____

COMMON CORE
STATE STANDARDS
W.6.1–
W.6.10

(continued)

Habitat

6.   Depending on the type, cnidarians can live in various parts of the sea. Some are bottom-dwellers and are attached to the ocean floor. Bottom-dwelling cnidarians are polypoids, which means their tentacles and mouth face up. Other types roam the sea at will. Free-swimming cnidarians are medusoids, which means their tentacles and mouths face down.

Impact

7.   Most cnidarians are not harmful to humans. Their stingers cannot usually penetrate human skin. Jellyfish are a type of cnidarian that can, at times, be dangerous. Jellyfish can deliver stings that are extremely painful and crippling to humans. Some jellyfish stings are so powerful that they can be fatal. Fortunately, however, most jellyfish stings yield only a mild rash like that caused by poison ivy.

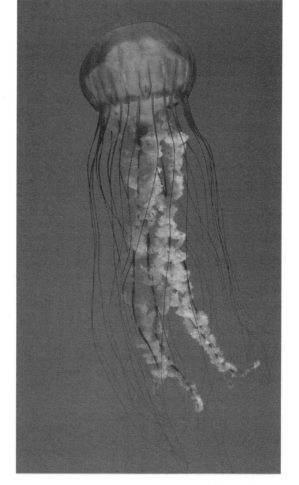

(continue to next passage)

COMMON CORE
STATE STANDARDS
W.6.1–
W.6.10

Name_____ Date_____

(continued)

Jellyfish Blooms—Is It Our Fault?

1. Hundreds of species of jellyfish float in the world's oceans. Their recent behavior has given scientists cause for concern, however. Blooms, or swarms, of jellyfish have been appearing in areas of the world where they have never been seen before.

2. Jellyfish blooms can be dangerous, especially if the jellyfish is a large species. A jellyfish bloom can extend for miles across an ocean. Some blooms can get so thick that there are more jellyfish than water. A jellyfish bloom can damage other forms of sea life. It can affect human industries such as fishing and tourism by tearing nets and damaging equipment. Jellyfish within a bloom can sting tourists swimming in the oceans. Large blooms can clog cooling water intakes at power plants, which can lead to power outages. Jellyfish blooms have been causing problems throughout the world since 1990. From Spain to Japan, blooms have become a subject of concern within the scientific community.

3. The Sea of Japan has seen the most extreme of all jellyfish blooms. Giant jellyfish known as Nomura's jellyfish have bloomed, creating serious problems for Japan's fishing industry. These jellyfish not only break fishermen's nets, but also crush the fish or poison them with their tentacles. Some of these massive creatures are 7 feet in diameter and weigh nearly 600 pounds. In 2009, a fishing boat capsized when its crew tried to reel in a net full of Nomura's jellyfish.

4. Many scientists believe that human activities cause jellyfish blooms. Blooms most likely occur in areas with environmental damage, which leads scientists to suspect that people may be indirectly responsible for this strange jellyfish behavior.

5. Global warming has increased ocean temperatures. Jellyfish tend to gather in warmer waters where they reproduce. When waters are warmer for a longer period of time, their reproductive season is extended, which means more jellyfish are born.

6. Overfishing might also be to blame. Overfishing eliminates some of the jellyfish's predators and food competitors. Forage fish, such as sardines and herrings, compete with jellyfish for food resources. Removing more of these fish from the ocean leaves more food for the jellyfish. Other factors that have helped jellyfish thrive include nutrients poured into coastal waters from waste and sewage runoff, which jellyfish eat, and the development of coastal structures such as piers and marinas, which provide habitats for baby jellyfish.

Common Core Writing to Texts Grade 6 • ©2014 Newmark Learning, LLC

Name_____ Date_____

COMMON CORE
STATE STANDARDS
W.6.1–
W.6.10

Argument Prompt

Do you think the jellyfish that make up a bloom are polypoids or medusoids? Use information from both texts to support your opinion.

Informative/Explanatory Prompt

Explain why a jellyfish bloom is harmful to people. Use facts and quotations from both the student encyclopedia and "Jellyfish Blooms—Is It Our Fault?" to support your explanation.

Narrative Prompt

Write a story about a character who has just seen a jellyfish bloom while swimming in the ocean. Write your story in the first person.

Name_____ Date_____

Read the passages.

Celebrating the New Year in America

1. The United States begins celebrating the new year on December 31. This is the last day of the year and is known as New Year's Eve. Festivities usually begin a few hours before midnight and include parties, parades, live performances, and other celebrations.

2. Traditionally, people count down the final seconds of New Year's Eve and then shout "Happy New Year!" Many exciting activities take place on New Year's Eve in America.

3. One of the most popular New Year's Eve Celebrations is held in the glowing Times Square intersection located in central New York City. Several city blocks are sectioned off to make room for the hundreds of thousands of people who come to the city to celebrate. Audiences are treated to an array of live musical performances and celebrity guest appearances. The event is broadcast live on news channels throughout the country, so viewers can watch at home.

4. New Year's Eve in Times Square involves the annual "ball drop." A minute before midnight, a giant lighted ball is dropped from the top of a pole attached to a tall building. The ball,

(continued)

Name_____ Date_____

(continued)

which is made of glass and weighs more than 1,000 pounds, descends slowly down the pole as the crowd counts down to midnight. It disappears behind the building when the clock strikes twelve. Then the crowd starts to cheer and shout "Happy New Year!" People throw confetti into the air and hug and kiss each other in celebration.

5. Once the clock has struck midnight, many people sing a traditional Scottish song called "Auld Lang Syne." The expression means "the old days gone by." The song was written by the Scottish poet Robert Burns in the eighteenth century.

6. After this song is sung, the festivities usually end, and everyone goes home.

7. Many Americans have the following day off. On New Year's Day, people spend time relaxing at home or visiting family and friends. People often watch football games on television while enjoying plenty of food and drink.

8. Many people watch the Rose Bowl, a championship football game held on New Year's Day each year. The game is preceded by the Tournament of Roses parade, an artistic celebration that includes marching bands and floats. The parade has a different theme each year.

9. A common New Year's Day custom is to make a list of resolutions. These resolutions are promises people make to themselves, agreeing to do or not do specific things. Resolutions are meant to improve a person's life in the year to come.

(continue to next passage)

Name_____ Date_____

(continued)

Celebrating the New Year in China

1. One of the oldest New Year's Day celebrations is the Chinese New Year. The Chinese New Year, also known as the spring festival, has many traditions. It is the most important celebration in the Chinese calendar. The Chinese New Year is meant to celebrate the start of new life and the beginning of plowing and sowing season.

2. In China, New Year celebrations begin on the first day of the lunar new year, which is in January or February. The festivities last until the fifteenth of the month, when the moon is at its brightest. Since Chinese calendars follow the lunar cycle, each month is as long as one cycle of the moon. Years are also grouped into twelve-year cycles. Each year is named after one of the twelve animals of the Chinese zodiac. For instance, the year 2012 was the year of the dragon, and the year 2013 was the year of the snake.

3. New Year's Eve takes place on the last day of the last month of the Chinese calendar. New Year's Eve is usually a much quieter event than New Year's Day. Families gather at home for a big meal of traditional Asian cuisine. They wear all-red clothing as a symbol of fire. Before they dine, a family must do its spring cleaning to sweep away any bad luck remaining in the house. Family members then decorate the house with paper scrolls containing words of good luck such as "happiness" and "wealth."

4. At midnight, people set off fireworks, and then go to sleep anticipating the exciting festivities of the New Year. When children awake on New Year's Day, they find a red envelope filled with money and candy under their pillow. The first week of celebrations involve visiting family and friends. Together, they fulfill traditions meant to bring good luck. The second week continues with more parties and feasting.

5. The celebration is capped off with the lantern festival, which takes places on the evening of the fifteenth day of the lunar new year. People decorate paper lanterns with scenes from Chinese history and legends. They then hang the glowing lanterns in their windows or carry them into the light of the full moon. Young men dance around the streets with a long paper dragon collecting money. This is called the dragon dance. If people want to say "Happy New Year!" in Chinese, they say "*gung hei fat choi*!"

Name_____ Date_____

COMMON CORE
STATE STANDARDS
**W.6.1–
W.6.10**

Argument Prompt

Would you rather celebrate New Year's Eve in China or America? Why? Support your opinion with details from both texts.

Informative/Explanatory Prompt

How is the Chinese New Year celebration different from the American New Year celebration? Use facts from both texts to support your explanation.

Narrative Prompt

Write a story about a boy or girl from China who celebrates New Year's Eve at Times Square in New York City.

Common Core
State Standards

W.6.1

W.6.4

W.6.5

Name_____ Date_____

Argument Organizer

Position Sentence:

Reason 1:	**Reason 2:**	**Reason 3:**
Reason 1 Evidence:	**Reason 2 Evidence:**	**Reason 3 Evidence:**

Restate position:

Name_____ Date_____

COMMON CORE
STATE STANDARDS
W.6.1
W.6.4
W.6.5

Argument Organizer

Position Sentence:

Reason 1:	**Reason 2:**	**Reason 3:**
Reason 1 Evidence:	**Reason 2 Evidence:**	**Reason 3 Evidence:**

Restate position:

Name_____ Date_____

Common Core
State Standards

W.6.2

W.6.4

W.6.5

Name_____ Date_____

Informative/Explanatory Organizer

Main Idea:

Evidence/details:

Evidence/details:

Main Idea:

Evidence/details:

Evidence/details:

Evidence/details:

Evidence/details:

Evidence/details:

Name_____ Date_____

Common Core
State Standards
W.6.2
W.6.4
W.6.5

Name_____ Date_____

Informative/Explanatory Organizer

Topic:

Main Point:	**Details:**
Main Point:	**Details:**
Main Point:	**Details:**

Name_____ Date_____

COMMON CORE
STATE STANDARDS

W.6.3

W.6.4

W.6.5

Name_____ Date_____

Narrative Organizer

Characters:	**Setting:**

Goal:

Major Events:

Ending/Resolution:

COMMON CORE
STATE STANDARDS
W.6.3
W.6.4
W.6.5

Name_____ Date_____

Narrative Organizer

Characters:

Setting:

Details from Stories I Read:

Events:

Problem:

Resolution:

COMMON CORE
STATE STANDARDS
W.6.1–
W.6.5

Name_____ Date_____

✔ Writing Checklist: Argument

- ❏ I stated a strong claim or point of view.
- ❏ I supported this claim with clear, well-organized reasons and evidence from the text or texts.
- ❏ My evidence is credible and shows an understanding of the topic.
- ❏ I used words and phrases to clarify the relationship between my claim and reasons.
- ❏ I used a formal voice in my argument.
- ❏ I provided a concluding statement or section that follows the argument I presented.
- ❏ I reviewed my writing for good grammar.
- ❏ I reviewed my writing for capitalization, punctuation, and spelling.

✔ Writing Checklist: Informative/Explanatory

- ❏ I started with a clear introduction to the topic.
- ❏ I grouped related information in paragraphs.
- ❏ I developed my topic with relevant facts, definitions, concrete details, quotations, or other information and examples from the text or texts.
- ❏ I used transition words and signal language to support the relationships among ideas.
- ❏ I used precise language and terminology to explain the topic.
- ❏ I used a formal voice.
- ❏ I wrote a conclusion related to the information I presented.
- ❏ I reviewed my writing for good grammar.
- ❏ I reviewed my writing for capitalization, punctuation, and spelling.

Common Core
State Standards
**W.6.1–
W.6.5**

Name_____ Date_____

✔ Writing Checklist: Narrative

❑   I established a setting or situation for my narrative.

❑   I introduced a narrator and/or characters.

❑   I organized my narrative into a sequence of unfolding events.

❑   I used dialogue and description to develop events and show how characters respond to them.

❑   I used transitional words to show my sequence of events.

❑   I used concrete words and phrases and sensory details to describe events.

❑   I wrote a conclusion to the events in my narrative.

❑   I reviewed my writing for good grammar.

❑   I reviewed my writing for capitalization, punctuation, and spelling.

Rubrics and Assessments

Using the Rubrics to Assess Students and Differentiate Instruction

Use the Evaluation Rubrics on the next page to guide your assessment of students' responses. The rubrics are based on the Common Core State Standards for writing. Similar rubrics will be used by evaluators to score new standardized assessments.

After scoring students' writing, refer to the differentiated rubrics on pages 130–135. These are designed to help you differentiate your interactions and instruction to match students' needs. For each score a student receives in the Evaluation Rubrics, responsive prompts are provided to support writers. These gradual-release prompts scaffold writers toward mastery of each writing type.

• For a score of 1, use the Goal-Oriented prompts.

• For a score of 2, use the Directive and Corrective Feedback prompts.

• For a score of 3, use the Self-Monitoring and Reflection prompts.

• For a score of 4, use the Validating and Confirming prompts.

Using Technology

If you choose to have students use computers to write and revise their work, consider these ways to support online collaboration and digital publishing:

• Google Drive facilitates collaboration and allows teachers and peers to provide real-time feedback on writing pieces.

• Wikis enable students to share their writing around a common topic.

• Audio tools enable students to record their works (podcasts) for others to hear on a safe sharing platform.

• Student writing can be enriched with images, audio, and video.

Evaluation Rubrics

Student _____   Grade _____

Teacher _____   Date _____

Argument				
Traits	**1**	**2**	**3**	**4**
The writer introduces the argument by stating a strong claim.				
The writer supports claim(s) with clear reasons and relevant evidence, using credible sources and demonstrating an understanding of the topic or text.				
The writer uses words, phrases, and clauses to clarify the relationships among claim(s) and reasons.				
The writer provides a concluding statement or section that supports the position.				
The writer establishes and maintains a formal style.				
The writer demonstrates command of grade-appropriate conventions of standard English.				

Informative/Explanatory				
Traits	**1**	**2**	**3**	**4**
The writer includes a strong introduction.				
The writer organizes ideas, concepts, and information, using strategies such as definition, classification, comparison/contrast and cause/effect.				
The writer uses relevant facts, definitions, concrete details, quotations, or other information and examples to develop his or her points.				
The writer uses appropriate transitions to connect ideas within categories of information.				
The writer provides a concluding statement or section that follows from the information presented.				
The writer establishes and maintains a formal style.				
The writer demonstrates command of grade-appropriate conventions of standard English.				

Narrative				
Traits	**1**	**2**	**3**	**4**
The writer establishes a context and introduces a narrator and/or characters and organizes an event sequence that unfolds naturally.				
The writer uses narrative techniques, such as dialogue, pacing, and description, to develop experiences, events, and ideas.				
The writer uses transition words, phrases, and clauses to signal shifts from one time frame or setting to another.				
The writer uses precise words and phrases, relevant descriptive details, and sensory language to convey experiences and events.				
The writer provides a conclusion that follows from the narrated experiences or events.				
The writer demonstrates command of grade-appropriate conventions of standard English.				

Key			
1–Beginning	**2–Developing**	**3–Accomplished**	**4–Exemplary**

Argument

TRAITS	1: Goal-Oriented
The writer introduces the argument by stating a strong claim.	When I start an argument, I state my claim or point of view. I need to tell exactly what my view is. After reading this prompt, I can state my position as _____.
The writer supports claim(s) with clear reasons and relevant evidence, using credible sources and demonstrating an understanding of the topic or text.	I need to think of two or three good reasons to support my claim. My claim about this prompt is _____. I'll jot down the evidence I need to support my claim. Then I'll go back to my writing and include them.
The writer uses words, phrases, and clauses to clarify the relationships among claim(s) and reasons.	I need to link my reasons together using words and phrases, such as *because, therefore, since* and *for example*. I am going to look for places where I can add these words and phrases.
The writer provides a concluding statement or section that supports the position.	When I finish writing an argument, I need to finish with a strong statement that supports my whole argument. When I conclude this argument, I can restate my claim as _____.
The writer establishes and maintains a formal style.	When I write an argument, I want to sound confident and official when I make a claim. I will do this by using a formal and serious tone.
The writer demonstrates command of grade-appropriate conventions of standard English.	I am going to read through my writing to make sure that my pronouns are in the proper case. I will read through my whole argument to make sure that I have spelled words correctly.

2: Directive and Corrective Feedback	3: Self-Monitoring and Reflection	4: Validating and Confirming
Reread the first sentences of your writing. Then go back and reread the prompt. Did you clearly state a claim that answers the prompt? Revise your statement to make it clear and focused.	Tell me how you chose ____ as your claim. How can you make your position clearer for the reader?	I can see that your position is ____. You made your claim very clear. That got me to pay attention to the issue.
What are your reasons for your claim? Find supporting details and evidence in the text for each reason. Group these ideas together in separate paragraphs.	How did you decide to organize your ideas? Did you identify the information that was most relevant to your claim? How did you do this?	You included some strong, relevant evidence to support your claim.
I notice that you have more than one reason to support your claim. What words can you add to show the reader that you are moving from one reason to another?	Show me a part of your argument where you link ideas using words and phrases. Show me a part where you could improve your writing by using linking words or phrases.	The words and phrases ____ and ____ are very effective at linking together the connection between your opinions and reasons. They help me understand your ideas.
Reread the last sentences of your argument. Does it end by restating your point of view? Go back and look at your claim. How can you reinforce this idea in your conclusion?	How does your conclusion support your claim or the position that you have taken? Is there a way you could make this conclusion stronger?	Your concluding section clearly supports your point of view. You've really convinced me that your claim makes sense.
Let's read this paragraph again. Are there words that do not sound like words you would use in a formal setting? Let's change them to sound more formal.	Tell me what you did to make your style sound formal.	I notice how you sounded like an authority on the topic. I liked how your tone was serious.
Read that sentence again. Does it sound right to you? Your pronoun is ambiguous. How should you edit that?	Show me a place in your writing where you used commas correctly. What rule of punctuation did you apply?	Your argument included many varied sentences which you punctuated correctly.

Informative/Explanatory

TRAITS	1: Goal-Oriented
The writer includes a strong introduction.	When I start an informational/explanatory text, I introduce my topic. I'm going to think about what I want my readers to know about ____. Then I create a main idea statement.
The writer organizes ideas, concepts, and information, using strategies such as definition, classification, comparison/contrast and cause/effect.	It is important that I group ideas together in an order that makes sense. I am going to categorize my information to help me structure the parts of my informative/explanatory text. I am hoping to organize my writing in a ____ format.
The writer uses relevant facts, definitions, concrete details, quotations, or other information and examples to develop his or her points.	I need to find facts and details from the text to support my points. I can go back to the text and underline parts that I think will help my writing. Then I will include them in my informative/explanatory text.
The writer uses appropriate transitions to connect ideas within categories of information.	I need to connect my ideas together using linking words, such as *also, another, and, more,* and *but*. I am going to look for places where I can add these words and phrases.
The writer provides a concluding statement or section that follows from the information presented.	When I finish writing an informative/explanatory text, I need to summarize my ideas in a conclusion. When I conclude, I can look back at my main idea statement, then restate it as ____.
The writer establishes and maintains a formal style.	I need to sound like the expert in this informative/explanatory text. I will use language that is formal. I will not use slang or write it in a voice I would use when talking with my friends.
The writer demonstrates command of grade-appropriate conventions of standard English.	I will make sure I have used quotation marks correctly when I've quoted directly from the text.

Common Core Writing to Texts Grade 6 • ©2014 Newmark Learning, LLC

2: Directive and Corrective Feedback	3: Self-Monitoring and Reflection	4: Validating and Confirming
How could you introduce your topic in a way that tells exactly what you will be writing about?	Take a look at your main idea statement. Do you feel that it clearly introduces your topic?	Your main idea statement is clearly ____. That introduction helped me understand exactly what I was going to read about.
Put your facts and details into categories. These categories can be the sections of your informative/explanatory text.	How did you decide to organize your ideas? Did you look at an organizing chart? How did it help you?	You organized your informative/explanatory text into [number] well-defined sections.
What are your main points? Find supporting details and evidence in the text for each point.	Have you included all of the facts you wanted to share about ____?	You included some strong facts, definitions, and details to support your topic.
Let's read this paragraph. I see two related ideas. How can you link these ideas together?	Show me a part of your informative/explanatory text where you could improve your writing by using transitions.	The words and phrases ____ and ____ are very effective at linking together ideas.
Reread the last sentences of your informative/explanatory text. Do they restate your main idea?	Show me your concluding statement. Is there a way you could make this conclusion stronger?	After I read your conclusion, I felt I had really learned something from your writing.
You are using "I" throughout your informative/explanatory text. Go back and revise your writing, so that the voice is not so personal.	Show me a part where you felt you had the right style for an informative/explanatory text.	I notice how you kept your own thoughts, feelings, and opinions out of the report and just told the facts in a formal tone.
Read that sentence again. Does it sound right to you? Some parts of your sentence do not agree. How should you edit that?	Show me a place where you made a correction. What was wrong and how did you fix it?	Your informative/explanatory text included many varied, complex sentences.

Narrative

TRAITS	1: Goal-Oriented
The writer establishes a context and introduces a narrator and/or characters and organizes an event sequence that unfolds naturally.	I will use a sequence of events chart to jot down the events I will write about. I will record details from the text I have already read. I will include those details in my new narrative.
The writer uses narrative techniques, such as dialogue, pacing, and description, to develop experiences, events, and ideas.	I want to include descriptions in my narrative. I will write down precise words that will help my readers picture what I am writing about. Then I will include these in my narrative.
The writer uses transition words, phrases, and clauses to signal shifts from one time frame or setting to another.	When I write a narrative, I need to use signal words so that my reader does not get confused. I will add words and phrases such as *first, then, the next day,* and *later that week* to help my reader understand the order of events.
The writer uses precise words and phrases, relevant descriptive details, and sensory language to convey experiences and events.	I will reread to look for words I have overused. Varying my word choice and making my words and phrases more precise will make my narrative more interesting to my readers.
The writer provides a conclusion that follows from the narrated experiences or events.	I am going to reread the ending of my narrative to make sure that it gives the reader a feeling of closure. I need to concentrate on how the problem in the narrative is solved.
The writer demonstrates command of grade-appropriate conventions of standard English.	I am going to read through my narrative to make sure that I formed and used both regular and irregular verbs correctly.

Common Core Writing to Texts Grade 6 • ©2014 Newmark Learning, LLC

2: Directive and Corrective Feedback	3: Self-Monitoring and Reflection	4: Validating and Confirming
Think of events that will lead from the problem to the resolution. You've decided to write about ____. Now think of the sequence of events you will include.	What graphic organizer could help you organize your narrative events? Tell me how you went about organizing your narrative.	The events you organized lead to a [fun, surprising, etc.] resolution.
Imagine that you're a character. What's happening in the narrative? What do you have to say to other characters? What do you have to say about the events?	How could you give each character a different voice in the dialogue?	I can visualize where your narrative takes place. You've included some nice descriptive details.
Let's read this paragraph. Is it clear to the reader when all the action is taking place? What words could you add to help the reader's understanding?	Show me where you used sequence signal words in your narrative. Show me a place where you could use signal words to make the order of events clearer.	The phrase ____ gave a nice transition between ____ and ____.
Notice the [action words, descriptive words] in your narrative. How could you make them stronger?	Show me where you revised some words to make the [experiences, events] clearer. How did your revision help?	I notice that you used [the idiom, description, figurative language, etc] to develop the character's dialogue. That really helped me hear the character's voice.
Let's read the ending of your narrative. Does it show how the problem is solved? Is there something you can add to make sure the reader feels as if the narrative piece is over?	Show me how your ending gives the reader a feeling of closure. Are there any questions from the narrative that you feel were unanswered?	You've developed an interesting resolution to the problem in your narrative. It gives me a sense of closure.
I got confused about the sequence when ____. Take another look at your verb tenses. Make sure they are consistent.	Show me a place in your writing where your sentences could be better. What could you do to improve them?	Your narrative included a lot of dialogue, and you used punctuation correctly.

Editing/Proofreading Symbols

Mark	What It Means	How to Use It
ℓ	Delete. Take something out here.	We went to to the store.
∧	Change or insert letter or word.	San Francico, Calafornia my home.
#	Add a space here.	My familyloves to watch baseball.
◡	Remove space.	We saw the sail boat streak by.
ℒ	Delete and close the space.	I gave the man my monney.
¶	Begin a new paragraph here.	"How are you?" I asked. "Great," said Jack.
⌒	No new paragraph. Keep sentences together.	The other team arrived at one. The game started at once.
∼	Transpose (switch) the letters or words.	Thier friends came with gifts.
≡	Make this a capital letter.	mrs. smith
/	Make this a lowercase letter.	My Sister went to the City.
◯	Spell it out.	Mr. García has 3 cats.
⊙	Insert a period.	We ran home There was no time to spare
∧	Insert a comma.	We flew to Washington D.C.
∨	Insert an apostrophe.	Matts hat looks just like Johns.
⧵⧵ ⧸⧸	Insert quotation marks.	Hurry! said Brett.
?	Is this correct? Check it.	The Civil War ended in 1875. ?
STET	Ignore the edits. Leave as is.	Her hair was brown. STET

Common Core Writing to Texts Grade 6 • ©2014 Newmark Learning, LLC